# Field of Frogs

# Field of Frogs

## THE ILLUSION OF LOVE ON THE INTERNET

### R.G. GRAHAM

ADVOCATE HOUSE
SARASOTA, FLORIDA

For information regarding permissions, write to:
A Cappela Publishing
913 Tennessee Lane
Sarasota FL 34234

3 1969 02158 3116

LIBRARY OF CONGRESS CATALOGING-IN-PUBLICATION DATA:
Graham, R. J.
    Field of Frogs /  by R. G. Graham
    p.    cm.
    ISBN 978-0-9850202-6-2
1. Internet dating — Non-fiction.   2. Scams — Non-fiction.
3. Single women — Non-fiction.
I. Title.

Designed by Carol Tornatore

First Edition

Printed in the United States of America

*I believe a journey is a voyage that takes you somewhere you want to go, to find something you think you do not have. What you learn along the way can make all the difference in what you seek. My honest journey is a cautionary tale through the internet, navigating my own field of frogs.*

*Introduction*

$\mathcal{J}$ was a good (though feisty) Catholic girl growing up, and immediately after college married. Two children later, living now on St. Croix, my husband asked for a divorce. We had spent most of our married years growing in tediously different directions. It had been a twenty year succession of arguments which left me feeling unhappy, unfulfilled and at the end of my endurance. I was empty. I got through that with help from my children and several lovers, including, finally, the love of my life. It was ironic that just when I had finally found Vicente, someone who brought me tremendous happiness after so many years, and the freedom to enjoy this love, our relationship would end. Unfortunately there were problems with this great love, so now that my children were grown, in the dawn of my sixties, I moved to Florida.

I had created the opportunity for a new beginning. I chose a community where everyone would be new and therefore the playing field would be level. I had not considered that we live in a couples' world. Life is easy and fine *if* you are part of a couple. I was alone and life was less easy and far less fine than I had hoped. There was only so much fussing and shuffling of furniture I could do with the house and when that was finished there was no one around to appreciate my efforts. No one to pay a compliment, or tell me my workout routine was paying off. No one to appreciate my efforts to keep myself looking attractive. I was still alone.

One late afternoon in Florida I poured myself a glass of wine and curled up on the sofa to enjoy my new and very different view of a setting sun. An occasional Osprey appeared to say hello as it flew low to grab its dinner from the lake. A lazy peaceful time of day. It would be another quiet evening. Far too quiet and with too much time to remember a very different life.

I literally knew everyone on St. Croix and during my more than thirty years there I had been totally connected to the community in which I lived and worked. I had enjoyed an exciting career in the hospitality industry. I had accumulated a great number of close friends and when you are on an island your friends also become your family. I had felt appreciated and accepted. I had also been deeply in love and sharing a wonderfully full life as part of a couple. All that had changed.

"I am officially and decidedly *over* this move to Florida." I had phoned my old and dear friend Delsey in disgust.

"There's nothing to do," I continued, celebrating my pity party over a second glass of wine. "No exciting job, no projects, no kids to take care of, no man in my life, no one to talk to around here except an occasional neighbor on the street. I don't feel connected to this place at all. I feel irrelevant."

"I felt the same way when I first moved here." Delsey had come to Florida a few years before I did.

"You forget one thing, Delsey, you have Rob. You are married. I'm rambling around in this house alone and it's making me nuts. There's stuff I would love to have help with here and there and that's hard to find, often there's no one around to even to talk to. There are places I'd love to go but don't want to go alone, there's no one to share my life with, maybe I should go back to the island. I miss having a man in my life. I really miss my old life!"

"Absolutely not!" Delsey was adamant about getting all of her friends safely relocated back to the states. "That's just not an option. You moved here for a reason, it was the right reason so we just need for you to find somebody to share this new life with."

"You make it sound so easy." I always admired her positive attitude but perhaps she had oversimplified things this time.

"All I know is that I've put up my last Christmas tree by myself, and I'm becoming a pathetic person."

"Oh for God's sake, you're not pathetic you're just lonely and you need to meet the right person!"

"That's easier said than done. I'm not in the workplace, I'm not picking up kids at school or running PTA meetings. Everyone in this place is married, and finding a man seems a piss poor reason for going to church, so what do you suggest?" I threw that out as a challenge because I felt I had covered all the bases.

"There's always the internet." Delsey had mentioned that to me many times in the past and it was always the place of last resort. *Was this it, was I at that place of last resort?*

"I had never thought much of going online to "meet" someone on a  computer screen. So I'm really not into the whole idea of being online. My romantic notion is simple: someday, somewhere, Mr. Wonderful would be across the room and the squishy feeling of seeing my "special someone" would come over me and that would be that."

"I understand that, Gay, but that someday and somewhere has not happened, and Mr. Wonderful is nowhere to be seen. So you have to try something different."

"I know.  I'm not sure where to start and I'm really not sure if online is the place I want to be."

"If you want different results, you have to try something different. Isn't that what you were always telling me, Gay?"

Okay, maybe I had said that. It's important to recognize that while I was not a fan of online dating, I had to acknowledge that it was hugely popular. The number one way to meet people, particularly in the over-fifty group. So maybe I was a bit behind the times. Maybe there was something about this online business that I could learn.

A week after that phone conversation I invited Delsey, her husband Rob, and our very good friend Sam for dinner. We had all been close friends on the island where we had lived, loved, and left within a five year period of each other. We all made the decision to relocate to Florida for different reasons and had remained best friends.

Somewhere between dinner and dessert that night, Delsey decided that Sam and I should appear on her local television program to share thoughts and experiences about our various relationships, the perils of dating after fifty . . . and the possible advantages and disadvantages of dating online. Even though we had been close friends for twenty years, there are some things a person would not or should not do, even for friends. And Sam's reaction was swift.

"No," he said without hesitation. My reaction was similar and I added, "Hell no!"

One week later Sam and I were still shaking our heads no as we entered the taping studio of the local television station. Delsey introduced us to her viewing audience and the cameras rolled.

*Part One*

# The Gift

Delsey moved deftly through the program, reading from her well prepared comparisons of the various dating sites. Each was geared to a slightly different audience; some were for specific religious groups, others for gays and lesbians, some targeted compatibility, still others fancied the chemical attraction. A plethora of choices. A wealth of information. An abundance of perspective internet users for these sites and a big black hole that swallowed everyone together in one huge common mouthful, referred to as cyberspace.

I interrupted Delsey's presentation with the question,

"Do they have any sites dedicated to people who might be allergic to marriage?" Delsey controlled her smile but the camera man could be heard chuckling out loud in the distance as he tried to stabilize his now jiggling camera.

"No, I don't think so, but perhaps you could somehow indicate that on the questionnaire and bio that you fill out." *Surely she isn't thinking that I would ever be filling out such a questionnaire. By "you" she has to mean the general audience.*

Delsey, in her role as moderator, occasionally would glance over the top of her pink polka dotted reading glasses to ask us questions or seek confirmations on her findings, and we did our best to answer enthusiastically.

"Have you ever had any experience with any online dating sites?"

*Come on Sam, you can answer this one, you told me you were on one of these things. Just because she's looking at me doesn't mean you can't answer the damned question.* Sam's silence was deafening and so slowly I blurted the confession I had tried to forget

"I did try one of the sites you mentioned about a year ago. I'd received a call from a neighbor. She'd just received a three day free offer to sign up online and find her Mr. Wonderful. She suggested I do the same and when I saw the same offer in my inbox I decided to at least give it a three day trial."

"So how did that work out for you?" I knew Delsey would have to ask me that. I was reluctant to tell her.

"Actually, it was exactly what I had expected it might be. I didn't think that any of these men would be of interest to me." *That was tactful enough wasn't it?*

"Why not?" Delsey asked. A reasonable question but she could be annoying, like an attractive Pitt bull with lipstick. *Why not? We're on television for the love of Pete, how can I be tactful with this now?* "Well, none of them had the look that I found attractive. I also thought the things they were interested in—hobbies, weekend activities, vacations— were just not things that would work for me." Still trying to save the answer, I continued:

"So, even though there was nothing unsuitable about any of them, there was nothing that grabbed my attention, or made my heart flutter."

"And you believe that you need someone that does that for you?"

"Yes, I really need the hook that captures my attention and makes me want to get to know them better. Their likes, dislikes, something that I could relate to." *This is not going well, I have nothing to contribute to this. That was three days out of my life. I wasn't into it then, I'm not into it now. How long is this damned program supposed to last anyway? I feel like I've been talking for hours, and what's up with silent Sam all of a sudden?*

Reading my mind, Delsey turned to Sam and deliberately posed the next question to him.

"Tell us about *your* experiences online, Sam."

There it was. Finally. *He'd told me about a few weird things once and I'm sure he was speaking about himself and not one of his friends. This would be good.*

"I really have not ever had any experience myself with online dating sites, but I have known people who have." *What a cop out. I didn't see it coming at all but Sam is still working in this community and I guess he has to, or feels he has to protect his privacy and his personal life. Tragic that he has to be so guarded about being gay, he's such an outstanding person.*

"Is there any reason, Sam, that you never decided to try one of these sites?"

"The information that I got from my various friends who had tried them made me realize that this was not the format that I would find positive for myself. I put it out of my mind entirely." *Thank God, that seems like a great way to end the show. Two guests, neither is remotely interested in online dating because it's unnatural and often freaky. Now let's all go home!*

Sam had been thoughtful and cautious in his comments. He briefly discussed the pros and cons of all points of views he had received from his friends, and had decided it was not for him. Ditto for me. I had never really known anyone who had met someone online. Not ever. Not even years ago when online dating first became popular. I had told Delsey I had no experience with this stuff. Three days hardly would count, yet it gave me enough of a clue to know this was not for me.

Sam had tried really hard. I, on the other hand, felt from the beginning that I had nothing to contribute to this TV program. It seemed appropriate for me to participate and appear to be interested in a subject even if I knew absolutely nothing about it. *Thank God it's over. Now we can all go back to Delsey's house for happy hour.*

I tried really hard to sneak a peek at my watch to see how much longer I would be required to sit there with my ever-so-fake-smile, waiting for the chance to finally escape to Delsey's house for our post-show cocktails. It was a bribe, and it had worked. Finally, the wrap up. The proper thank you for our participation, the thank you to the viewing audience, which *hopefully* only numbered a scant handful. And then it hit.

Delsey removed her little pink readers, leaned forward and looked straight into the camera . . .

"Now," she said, "I have a surprise for my two guests."

*Here it comes, I thought. The sucker punch to the gut. The unanticipated, unwelcome offering of something very sinister.*

Delsey continued, ". . . I have taken the liberty of signing each of my friends here tonight to two dating sites that were mentioned during this program. All they have to do is promise to come back on this program in a few months and tell us about their experiences!"

There it was. It could have been worse, but I'm not sure how. I was trapped just as surely as a grizzly with his paw poorly placed and clamped painfully inside a sharp metal vice. I never saw it coming, but I could hear myself let out the great silent scream of a wounded animal.

Sam and I exchanged a glance that was unmistakable. It was excruciating pain mixed with fear of the unknown. It was impending doom. Terror.

Another series of really fake smiles and, with keys rattling nervously in hand. I made my way to the car.

Cocktails with Delsey and Rob consisted of two very strong belts of vodka with only enough tonic to improve the swallow. Incredulous glances and comments were exchanged and Delsey was convinced that she had not blindsided either Sam nor me with her gift offering.

"Neither one of you would ever have chosen to go on a dating site, we all know that!" She seemed almost proud of herself that she had pulled off such a coup.

"Delsey, if you knew that, then why the hell didn't you leave well enough alone?" I was curious about that one.

Delsey stood up, drink in hand and made her pronouncement.

"I firmly believe that online dating is the best chance to meet someone." There's that definite opinion of hers again.

"These people are out there but they are not going to come knocking on your door! You two need to get with the program and just find someone online!" *So what's wrong with someone knocking at our doors? As long as it's not the Latter Day Saints or a vacuum cleaner salesman, who cares? Besides, I've seen the local firefighters, and any one of them could knock on my door anytime.*

"Delsey, please tell me this isn't about trying to create yet another program for your television show." That would be beneath her, but a question I felt I had to ask.

"Heaven's no, look here you two, I've known you both for so long and you each have so much to offer, I really believe it's the best way to meet your fairy-tale handsome Prince. So I took the liberty of getting you both on the program, and then came up with the brilliant idea to give you each this little surprise. I only meant to help you with something you wouldn't help yourselves with, and that's the truth."

There was the rock. There was the hard place. There was the friendship with Delsey. We chose our friend.

I sucked down another vodka and headed for home.

# *Getting Ready for the Party*

*I* began the daunting task of navigating through the myriad of questions in preparation for creating a profile designed to introduce me to my Prince Charming. Worse than applications for passports or drivers licenses: height, body type, eye color, hair color; religious preference, education, job description; number of children, do you want children, (*at least they didn't ask if I wanted to keep the ones I already had*) and on and on it went. Your idea of a perfect first date; type of music you like; hobbies, interests, movies, books, pets —those were all fairly easy and obvious questions. (Did any of these things truly matter?) I guess if you were in your twenties and wanted to start a family it would be important to sort out the baby question in advance but I feel that the creators of this data base omitted more important questions that would get to the heart of a person's character and personality. I began questioning the questions. Why would anyone possibly *care* what my favorite color is, or if I preferred Italian over Mexican food? Asking if I preferred Italian over Mexican *men* would have made more sense to me.

What kinds of books did I like to read or did I like to cook. No questions about what makes me sad or happy, am I a well adjusted person, am I bipolar, currently in therapy, or ever been on the FBI watch list. I concluded that nobody cared about important things, which made me a tad nervous thinking that if nobody cared about these things then I would be trying to find Prince Charming in a pile of superficial fluff or clever lies. How would I know if he seemed to measure up to my criteria? I had given a great deal of thought to the qualities I wanted in a man and they were easy to name but a lot harder to find: kind, thoughtful, compassionate, good sense of humor, well educated, financially secure, well traveled, lover of animals, honest, sincere, charming, compatible, romantic, passionate, sensitive, sexual, attractive . . . and as a dear friend of mine told me having read my list, I should have simply asked if the man could walk on water. *When I reviewed the list it became abundantly clear why I was single!*

I finished my profile as honestly as I could. It was not full of cute sayings or dazzling adjectives. In my own opinion it was a bit lackluster. It is so much easier to be creative and witty when you are in the company of others. I did manage to accurately account for my likes, dislikes, interests, hobbies, and what qualities I was looking for in a man. *There goes that list again, maybe I would scare them off with that damned list, or maybe eventually someone would measure up.* I also managed to convey that I was a woman of substance with the serious intention of finding the right man. Bravely, with a click of a button, my profile was sent into cyberspace. Only time would tell.

Who was handling all this information? All the

fragments of profiles that were scattered into space? Who were the elves working in Santa's Workshop of online dating? Who was in charge of matching up interests, skills, education or even age? Computers can't reason. They only regurgitate information they have received. I told myself that ten to twenty years ago there were many reported success stories of people who met their partners online. That was then, however, and now the internet opens so many more doors for millions of people. Evidently forty-million people plus, use the internet for a dating or match making site today. Who would be coordinating all these millions of profiles, and who were these people? Where would they come from? Could it be that everyone would be looking for a mate? Maybe they were cheating on their wives and not divorced at all? Satisfied that this was like a bizarre field trip through space minus the chaperones, I accepted there would be no one checking anyone. The onus was on me to remain on my toes.

With some degree of anxiety, and a sprinkling of anticipation, I faced the computer squarely the next morning and there they were. In someone's mind for some unseen reason, these few forlorn and lonely look-ing men appeared in my inbox.

(Surely this was not what had cost me hours of homework the night before! Not to mention $49.95 per month.) I am not a superficial person, but even cereal boxes would have passed on the opportunity to print these pictures. Yet here they were, and they weren't pretty. They were all "searching for their soulmate."

*They probably had a soulmate and she dumped*

*them!) Someone, they say, who would enjoy long walks
with them on the beach. (In reality, a short walk to
the garage is probably more than old Ralph looked like
he could manage.) They all said they knew how to
treat a woman. (If they really knew how to treat a
woman, would they all be divorced now?) Looking for
someone online? Really?*

*To do what with, I wondered. Chances were good
it would not be looking for a long term relationship.*
They all want to go camping, hiking, skinny dipping —
(oh God please spare me *that* visual). Chuck looked
sleazy. Skinny dipping put it over the top. I could not
see myself relating to *any* of these men.

*My idea of camping would be a week at Caneel
Bay on the beach at St. John in the Virgin Islands.* They
said they liked to dance. John didn't resemble Gene
Kelley in the least.

*He probably meant a hoe-down at a trailer park.*
Looks can be deceiving, I know, I've heard it all my
life but this went beyond looks. The information, photos, activities, hobbies, everything was pathetic and
nothing that I felt I could work with. No one I could or
would even respond to. I believe what happened in this
particular Santa's Workshop section of cyberspace was
a random gathering of everyone within ten years of each
others age, regardless of geographic location. Even if I
had wanted to meet any of them, (which God knows I
did not) it would have been impossible based on where
they lived, never mind a distinct lack of matched interests. It went on like that for days. I thought it odd that
I could receive this many men in the inbox who were

totally inappropriate for me, my age, or my location. Surely my profile would not have appealed to this group. I can only assume I must have been fresh meat. (Charming!) I would open the page and hit delete. Open the page and hit delete. There was just no point in contacting any of them. (Probably no point in my even being on a dating site, which is what I told Delsey from the beginning.) So my initial days of online dating supported the public statement I had made on television, that no one had the look I wanted nor the interests that would match my own. After days of looking I came up empty, and discouraged.

The odds of finding The Prince on a site like this was an absurd notion from the beginning. The first thing is the visual impression. I am not superficial but I could not get beyond the photos I was seeing. On a chance that one *could* get beyond the first impression then there might be a chance to explore mutual interests and ideas. My mind ran to Alan, one of the pack who stood out, for the wrong reason. I wondered when it was that ball caps and "wifebeater" shirts had become the costume of choice for a dating site photo?

(At least Alan was probably telling the truth about not having a wife. No self respecting woman would have let Alan out of the house looking like that, let alone allow this photo to be taken). Many photos had men straddling motorcycles, or behind the wheel of a vintage car. That didn't do it for me. *Unless that guy was Marlon Brando or James Dean, no motorcycles please.* No, my Prince Charming was not in this group.

*This group looked like they could have settled for any 'double-bagger,' or even been okay with a woman who's face would force her to Trick or Treat over the phone. Too bad for me I was never on the cover of Sports Illustrated swimsuit edition or been a waitress at Hooters: then I might be having better luck!*

This whole process was disappointing and absurd but I had signed up to play. After hours of thought provoking work on that blasted profile, and being as honest as possible, I knew one thing. While I was being honest, the nagging doubt persisted that the mythical 'he' was somewhere skulking around dying his hair black, or attaching his graduation photo to his profile, and otherwise just lying his ass off. It is an unpleasant business. It is a scary, fascinatingly comedic process, in a dangerous sort of way. I was two days into it, and I hated it.

One day I decided it was time to check on Sam to see if his luck was any better than mine. I called. I heard. I was way ahead. Sam had found guys who were interested in piercings, tattoos, hot sex and motorcycle rides. Others who preferred handcuffs and mirrored ceilings.

"At least you were in contact with these guys to get this information Sam, I couldn't even do that!"

"Isn't that supposed to be how it works?"

"Yes. I am almost envious of your weird group which seems to trump my group of zeroes. These guys had been sent to me through space." (Lucky, lucky, me)

"This really was all a bad idea Sam, how the hell did we get into this mess in the first place?"

"It was your dinner party and Delsey's unabashed idea of how to create a different type of program for her audience"

"Well, I had a feeling that this would happen, although I wasn't thinking it would be quite as unappealing as it has become. I should say at least for me. I just had no idea this is how it would work."

"I didn't either," admitted Sam, "but I was willing to try, at least for Delsey's sake."

"I agree with you about Delsey. She was really convinced that this would work. I'm sorry for her sake it isn't going well at all."

"Well, I s'pose there's one way to look at it," (Sam always saw a bright side.)

What's that, Buddy, because I am not thinking this is going anywhere."

"The bright side is, at least we won't have to do another television program!"

"Right. You know, Sam, this dating site sends me a group of guys every day that remind me of stowaways on a railroad car, and you either throw them a line of encouragement or hope they jump off the train at the next stop!" (So far I had hoped they would all jump off at *any* stop, as long as it was not mine!)

"Sam, I've made a decision."

"Okay, do tell"

"If any of these men that I've had to look at these last few days lived across the street from me, I asked myself if I would even venture across the street to introduce myself and take them a fresh batch of muffins. When I couldn't answer that simple question with a yes,

I knew it was time to pull the plug." (*I have to add my muffins are really not too bad!*)

"So what does that mean now?" It seemed like Sam was feeling he might be left alone in the middle of our mutual mess if I bowed out.

"It means, dear Sam, that I have given it two days. I've hated every minute of it, it doesn't seem to be working, and it's making me feel bad for these sad souls. I'm done."

"Just like that?"

"Yes, just like that." Sam seemed a bit surprised but there's no denying logic.

"I do wish you well with all of this, Sam, and hope you have really good luck but I can't do this any more. It's a huge waste of time. I really am done."

I called the dating site in question, explained my situation and told the disinterested person on the other end that I needed to cancel my membership.

"Sorry, but this is not working for me. I am finished. Over. I am finished."

"Oh, I'm sorry you're not having any luck, but your three months have already been paid for so we'll just apply any remaining time over to the parent company. It looks like you'll have about two full months left on the contract and we can have you up and running in an hour."

There it was. Another paw in another trap. Was there no escaping any of this? Now it was confirmed; this *never* was a good idea. I called Sam. He commiserated with me. I loved Delsey, but I was ready to put a contract out on her life!

For anyone who had been out of a relationship as long as I had, Valentine's Day was just another day; the fourteenth day of the month. I never realized the coincidental significance: a commercial excuse to trade on those romantics who selected flowers, cards, or lacy intimates. For me it was just another day, but a day spent in my office busily writing down enough words to properly present a different profile to be posted on the new dating web site. Different web site, different process, somewhat different information. Different results, hopefully.

Easy to describe your friends, not so easy to describe yourself. Yet here I was again, trying to grab someone's attention by drawing them in to my personality and hoping that somehow a meeting with Mr. Wonderful would emerge, for even a simple cup of coffee. The new profile was completed. I began to reflect on the possible outcome of this computerized matchmaking. It all seemed so shallow but it was too late for me now; I was floating in cyberspace yet again. My calm, effortless, pleasant life, would soon be spiraling out of control.

# The Daily Five

They were called the "Daily Five". They could easily have been five guys you used to see on post office walls — wanted for something. (Not wanted for a long term relationship, trust me). Sadly they were last seen smiling back at me when I first went into my email. No, not again! Worse than dogs in a pound. Choose me, choose me!

*Good God No! Not even if you're scheduled to be euthanized tomorrow!*

It was the second time I had seen such an unfortunate collection of men. It was also the second time I realized that this whole online dating thing was a mistake. Judging by this morning's collection, a huge mistake!

I had to make a serious attitude adjustment to try to make this work. As a newbie to this process I dutifully read each profile. By the fifth and final, they had all morphed into one unpleasant blob, like a drawer full of partially used holiday candles, melted together after the festivities hoping to get something useable, . . . like one more melted glob of totally unusable candles.

According to this group, they were all divorced, looking for women twenty years younger than they were. None owned up to having any bad habits, most described themselves as 'good looking' or 'handsome,' and all knew exactly what women wanted and how to treat a woman. Again, doubtful information to the average reader. Describing your physical self and appearance to a person who is looking at the picture of what you are describing, takes a real skill, and a great deal of nerve.

*Don't any of these guys own a mirror?* The men are simply telling you what they think you want to hear, without realizing that I am the one who is seeing them. Their descriptions were brazen and totally inaccurate.

Jason described himself as liking to dance. That was somewhat encouraging, if I could believe him.

"Hey baby, I see you like to dance, maybe we could win a contest, I'm very good at it. Write me back." *Maybe I could believe him but his initial communication was less than stellar.*

"Maybe after we at least meet each other we could go dancing *sometime*, but entering a contest right now seems a bit out of sight." *I do love to dance but a big NO to this guy.*

How many men do you know who honestly like to dance? Women prefer this activity probably two to one, but it's mentioned with great frequency. So Jason now likens himself to Fred Astaire but I am *not* going to be his Ginger Rogers. *I am certain that Jason looks like he would prefer an evening with the remote control from the comfort of his recliner.*

Fred, from Nebraska, liked "walking on the beach in the moonlight." Really? I challenge anyone to go to any beach at sunset and find men just strolling up and down. I think the real truth is that by the time the moon makes its appearance most men are asleep on the sofa, mouth agape. Empty beer cans lined up and waiting for the woman to haul them away. I summoned my sense of humor and my nerve and fired off my first email to Fred.

"Hi Fred, I got your profile this morning and see you like walking on the beach. What beach do you prefer?"

"Hi yourself, I'm happy to hear from you, I like the beach around here"

"Fred, how is that beach convenient to where you live?"

"Hey — I go there sometime, and like it"

"Fred, I'm in Florida, I don't believe this is viable."

*Fred, you asshole, there is no beach in Nebraska. My geography is sure of that. You lose.*

They all mentioned how romantic they are; but cutting and pasting love poems found online and emailing them to you doesn't count.

"Roses are red violets are blue, if you will be mine I will be true to you."

This was an effort emailed to me from Ambrose.

*Who would name their kid Ambrose, and was this a real attempt to get my attention?*

It was happening again. I was feeling the cloud of a bad mistake looming overhead.

They all wanted to travel the world *with* that special someone, particularly if she puts it on *her* credit card. So, reading these profiles was not an encouraging exercise, by any means. Amusing maybe, but not encouraging. These men came in all shapes, sizes, colors, ages, and different geographic areas in spite of the rather specific questions you are asked to provide, to guide the dating site toward finding your perfect mate. So my first morning with the "Daily Five" was eye opening, amusing, pathetic, somewhat entertaining and very disappointing.

I reflected back to my list of desired qualities. I reviewed it carefully.

This task was finished. It was a long list but this was the kind of man I was looking for. This is what I wanted. This is who I was looking for. I refused to settle.

My final salvo was for the universe to track this guy down like a bloodhound, but if he was not right for me, I asked that he not be put in my path. I was very specific about that.

# Down the Path

Day One dawns. I arrive in my office that first morning armed with only a double mug of coffee and the best of intentions. Surprise! There are four faces out of five staring back at me and they look totally different from yesterday's collection. These men are all attractive, decidedly younger than I, yet definitely old enough to vote. I'm safe. Two of the three have "winked" at me. That means they have viewed my profile and photo, and decided that I am a possibility for them. The wink is to determine if I share their optimism. I did, on this occasion, and responded with a wink of my own. Things were looking up.

The fourth face made me feel creepy just looking at him, like maybe the orange shirt was really a federal prison issue, so I simply ignored number four. (I'm glad I catch on to things so quickly!)

Andy, however, caught my eye immediately. He had a handsome face, hair lightly greyed at the temples, looked great in his dark grey suit in the photo, and lived probably five miles up the road. His profile indicated he was an executive, financially secure, divorced, and seemed to share all the things I enjoyed. A good beginning I thought.

He asked for my email address so he could write to me. I obliged.

Jim was number two. He seemed quite keen, without my knowing exactly why at this early stage. My curiosity got the better of me as he was a bit of an entrepreneurial type and enjoyed traveling and earned a living buying objects abroad. Jim wanted to email me. I obliged.

Frank was the youngest of the group and had a son living at home. I was a bit more cautious about Frank. Although I was a pushover for a handsome face, there remained something about him that seemed a bit 'off' at first. He wanted to send me an email quite quickly. I ignored my initial reaction and obliged.

In what seemed to be a very short span of time indeed my inbox was full of messages from all of these guys. Interestingly enough they all expressed an interest to be more involved with the instant messaging system the web site sets up, so that you can 'chat' with each other frequently and for no cost, just in case someone was out of town. As it turned out, they *all* were out of town.

I did establish an email account to be used exclusively for the online dating which would minimize potential problems.

Frank was with his son in Nigeria, building an orphanage.

"I have no one to care for my son," he told me, "so I take him with me wherever I go because there's no one to care for him at home." That sounded like a difficult arrangement, particularly adding Nigeria into the equation.

"I do have someone that comes along with me to watch out for him and keep him up with his school work while I'm working." It took only one short 'chat' to determine that I did not want to play a mother role again to someone else's young school age child. I also would have difficulty with the child's tutor if he turned out to be a she. Perhaps the most compelling issue came the next day.

"I have this huge problem I really need your help with. I need a little assistance with this hotel bill here until my pay day, so my son and me won't be thrown out of this small hotel room."

(Quite clever, but not clever enough, so hopefully the Nigerian bush would welcome both of them, because I sure wouldn't.)

Delete.

Jim, number two, mentioned immediately that he was in Malaysia. "I'm over here buying furniture in Indonesia and some gem stones, and am preparing to leave the country when I finish my buying." His home was in northern Florida and he would soon be back.

"I hope to make it home soon, and I hope you will be waiting for me when I get there. We can arrange a way to meet then."

"Why don't you wait until you get back and we can take it from there." I thought that was a practical solution and who knew what would happen between now and whenever it was he might finish his work.

"I'm sure you're the perfect woman for me." *I'm sure to the contrary.*

"I can't imagine how you can say such a thing without ever meeting me."

"I always know these things immediately, and I'm sure you are the woman for me."

The 'chat' with him was tedious as I found myself waiting longer and longer for responses to simple questions and waiting the same amount of time for questions about me to be asked. They never were. I suggested on several occasions that I found the simple emails to be more productive.

"You can be free to express an entire train of thought without interruption."

*Assuming you have an entire train of thought and I won't have to wait for an hour to receive an answer to my question about you.*

The 'chat' was definitely more productive for him, particularly because I would furnish instant answers to his question. However it was the nature of his last concern that had me asking the big question. Really?

"I am going to be delayed for quite a while because they want to charge me excess money on the taxes and duty to leave the country."

Delete.

Andy, number one on this list, appeared to look like a gentleman. He too was working overseas as a design contractor for condominiums being built in Malaysia.

"I should be home very soon and we only live within a few miles of each other, I would like to get together with you then." He seemed to have some good qualities and seemed to be interested in getting to know me, and in the beginning he too was very fond of the 'chat.'

*The only one that lives remotely close to me, hopefully this will work.*

"I have two daughters who are living on their own, and I also have a little Maltese dog that I walk around the park. Maybe we could get together later and walk our dogs in the park." Somehow that sounded better than rescuing some bozo and his kid from the Nigerian bush or paying a lot of export taxes to the Indonesian government.

"What park do you usually go to?" There were a number of them in my area and I was curious which one he preferred. There was not an immediate answer. No identifying geographic location. Nothing but a long pause and an interruption of short duration.

"Give me a minute please."

(Here we go again with another of these damned pauses. I could have folded all the laundry by now and put it away. What the hell is he doing?)

I have no idea why that chat business is so popular. It only works when you have a lot to say, and the ability to say it, and move on to the next question without allowing light years to fill the void.

Finally, after a day, it was clear that Andy had also been 'chatting' with someone else who must have had more patience than I with the process, and little by little our communication slipped away, and I concluded he was not the right match for me. I did send him a final email regarding my thoughts, and I wished him well. (Sometimes my ingrained sense of good manners was a bit overused.) I was still curious about how he never came up with a name for that park.

Delete.

It had been a reasonably fun and certainly informative few days. Whoever would have believed that these good looking men would appear all on the same day, and be interested (for one reason or another) in initiating communication with me. While all of this had only occurred on my first day on this site, it was more encouraging than the last experience and so I was now cautiously optimistic.

It was really the second day that would change my life.

# *Wink*

*T*he day started like any other day; my best guy and four legged pal, Oliver, stretched lazily on his pillow next to mine, yawned, and rolled toward me to determine if my feet were creeping out from under the sheets just yet. When they did, Oliver, taking his cue, sprang down and shook out his fine curly hair, sat up smartly and gave me the look. I knew there was no time to dally with my normal ablutions; only time to jump into my street clothes, grab a hat, slide into my sneakers and hastily get to the front door. As was the norm, I collected the newspapers and tossed them back toward the house, then waited for Oliver to scan the street back and forth looking for his friends, and to make the final decision on which direction we would go. Left it was, and off we went, hoping to catch a glimpse of his pal Jack.

Jack's human mother had been the photographer for the photo I posted on the dating site, and she had been tracking the progress, or lack thereof, with interest.

"How's it going?" she asked each time we met.

Jack had become a good pal to Oliver, even though their size difference rendered them an amusing couple.

27

Jack was a Great Dane and Anatolian Shepherd mix. His size was impressive and his expression could be intimidating. By comparison, Oliver was a medium sized thirty pound Australian Labradoodle with an appealing face that peeked amusingly from an apricot colored cloud of curls, and had a smile that would melt even the coldest heart. The dogs would visit while we chatted.

"Nothing exciting so far," I told her, "but today is another day, and who knows what may happen. The last group looked decidedly better than the first group. I'll keep you posted."

No sign of Jack this morning so we walked alone together around a few blocks of the neighborhood. It's a great way to begin the day, to clear your head and inventory the necessary activities. Oliver serves as an excellent sounding board and while he never comes up with an alternative plan, he listens so intently to mine I'm certain he agrees with me.

"Today, Oliver, I will fix a quick breakfast, grab some coffee and head to the computer to check out what is swirling in the inbox from the night before, and I will take care of laundry, and manage to fit in a trip to the grocery store later on." He seemed reasonably interested in the agenda so far so I continued.

"Afternoon I will catch up on some odds and ends, take you for another walk, then hopefully have enough time left to relax and do a bit of reading." That was a plan, and all that remained was the execution.

"Are we ready, Buddy?" If I was ready then so was he. (This dog's brilliant, smarter than most men I know.

A fact that I would constantly be reminded of going forward.)

I put some cottage cheese into a bowl sprinkled that with some fresh blueberries, poured a mug of coffee and headed to my office.

The calendar at the bottom of my computer screen said February, fifteenth. That was all I saw except for a large yellow wink. That symbol was next to a good, handsome face which came rising up elegantly from a white dress shirt. This man had, easily, the broadest smile I had ever seen.

He was a fine looking gentleman. There was no doubt. He had 'the look' and as I studied his face I could feel a squishy feeling emerging.

"Oliver, come here and take a look at this guy, he's gorgeous." This was his nap time and his nod in my direction told me he heard me but was unimpressed. *How can you be unimpressed with a guy that looks like this?*

"Okay, stay where you are. I'll read you what it says. He's sixty years old, a veterinarian — (oh Buddy we have a perfect match for you too) — his annual income is around one hundred thousand dollars, (that will buy you lots of dog bones), he is divorced (she must have been nuts to divorce him), one child living on its own."

His expanded description of himself with a lengthy list of qualities, made me draw a deep breath. All the qualities I had included on my tediously long list and sent into cyberspace, had perhaps just returned to this very page, in Dr. Mark R. Smith's profile. I couldn't believe my good fortune.

"Oliver, I think I'm in luck. This guy seems fabulous, and looks even better." There was a place on that site to return the big yellow wink and I hit the 'submit' button faster than if I'd been playing the power ball lottery.

I stared at the profile and that smiling face for a very long time, allowing my thoughts to swirl. The interest in the remainder of my inbox, vanished. Instead, my head was filled with thoughts of this elegant looking man. This new wonderful looking man with the perfect credentials and great qualities that I was looking for. This man was speaking to me. I certainly felt entitled to this stroke of apparent good luck after the lackluster beginning.

Dr. Mark Smith, a professional, who was financially secure, available, handsome, possessed all the right qualities, and had an interesting profile. Hmmm. This was going to be a very good day.

Another mug of coffee is what I needed. That, and some time to reflect on what I had just read. I walked out of the office passing Oliver, curled into his favorite snooze position. I stopped by his head and reached down to give him a pat and as I did so, leaned down closer to him to remind him, out loud, of my previously mandated statement to the universe:

"If he is not right for me, do not put him in my path."

Oliver lifted his head and registered his agreement with his soft brown eyes, swished his great fox-like tail back and forth, and returned to his nap.

It didn't matter that he wasn't impressed. I was

impressed enough for both of us.

That afternoon I received a brief email from Dr. Mark Smith.

"You have no idea how grateful I am to have received the wink from you earlier. I feel like the luckiest man in the world. I am very eager to get to know you better and I do look forward to hearing from you again. I hope you have a lovely day, you sure have made mine wonderful."

He sent an attachment along with his message, another photo of himself, this one taken at a restaurant I would guess. He seemed to be happily surrounded by a sea of assorted wine and water glasses, suggesting this was not an intimate dinner for two, but rather a gathering of a group of friends obviously having a good time together. It made we wish I had been included in that party. I couldn't get over what a lovely looking man he was. Beautiful smile. High forehead, light brown hair, grey/green eyes, a strong square face; and somehow, I was more drawn to that photo, that face, that man, than even I cared to admit, much less understand.

Late afternoon I was back online again, checking for any additional message from Mark, and there it was.

"I was really very glad to hear from you. How did I get to be so lucky? You are such a pretty woman I have been thinking about you all day. It's kind of hard for me to get anything done since I saw you."

*I'm not going to tell you I have thought of nothing but you since I first saw your photo.*

"Would it be all right to add you to my contact list

so that we could begin to do instant messaging?" Mark was eager to get started.

I agreed and very shortly thereafter we began the process of getting to know each other online. Unlike my previous experience, Marks' chats were fast paced; answers and questions flying back and forth freely and quickly. Gone were the long pauses that left me wondering if the writer had abandoned the computer to hop a flight to Rio. It was not a perfect solution for getting to know a person but if someone was living in New York, as his profile indicated, and I was on the southwestern coast of Florida, as my profile clearly indicated, it was a viable solution for establishing a friendship before meeting that person. We chatted twice that day, answering each other's basic questions about children, divorces, work, when finally he asked if it would be possible for him to call me later that evening. I felt comfortable giving him my cell phone number. It was listed under my son-in-law's family plan, different name from mine, which I felt added a measure of privacy. He did not have my full name only my nickname given to me at birth. What could go wrong?  At precisely eight o'clock that evening I got to hear his voice.

" Hello Gay, this is Mark. Mark Smith." The voice was strong but the connection was very poor and I had to concentrate on the words to make sure I was hearing everything properly.

"Hi Mark, I'm glad to hear your voice." This was true although I faltered a bit because I noticed the call was coming in from Grand Prairie Texas.

"I was expecting you to be calling from New York. What are you doing in Grand Prairie Texas?"

I was also wondering how in the world the dating site could have included someone from New York to match with someone in Florida. A bit beyond the fifty mile suggested maximum radius, even for the *worst* student of Geography.

"I'm working here" he said, as if I should have figured that out all by myself.

"What are you working there doing exactly?" I was now quite curious how this relatively large leap from New York to Texas had occurred.

"I'm living and working here right now."

I continued to press on because confusion is difficult to unravel after a while.

"What kind of work are you doing there?"

"I'm a veterinarian you know, so I'm here working on the prevention of infectious diseases in livestock and their offspring."

I could see there were some questions looming up, and struggling through an awful connection, I pressed further.

"Oh, so you're a large animal veterinarian." It was beginning to make some sense now.

"Define large" he asked. I took that as a bit odd but there was something in his voice that I was struggling with as well as this blasted connection that was making clarity very difficult.

"As in cows." I thought my comeback was specific, if not witty.

"Yes," he said, "as in cows and other livestock."

"Why does your profile say you are in New York City?"

"Because," he started, "when I was visiting my

friend, who's also a vet in New York, he's the one who talked me into joining this dating site. He found his wife online and told me it was something I should do as well."

"I see," I said, when I wasn't sure if I really did or not.

"So how did you get from New York to Texas?" I still wanted to hear how that connected.

"I went where the work was." "I go to different places for different projects on assignment from time to time."

"So that would mean, that you don't have a practice where people stop into your office with your patients on the other end of a leash?"

Last time I was in New York I was not aware of herds of cattle moving down Broadway, so this had to be the only possible explanation.

"No, not any longer, I just do contract work." There was a bit of a pause and then he went on.

"This connection is really bad I can tell. Let me call you tomorrow sometime and we can go back to the instant messaging."

"I think that would be an improvement over this phone line." I agreed, and hung up; still wishing to be connected to that voice somehow. There was so much more I wanted to learn. Some dialect was present, it was familiar to me, although I couldn't make it out just yet,

I knew a bit more about him than I had before. Some of it seemed different from what was my normal frame of reference. Vets normally had a practice some-where and critters came to them. Mark clearly had a different specialty where he was undoubtedly doing a bit of research on infectious diseases as he said, and the critters were coming to him. One more thing to add to my list of things to research online.

I hung up the phone and got online immediately to see if I could make more sense of things with Google's help. Grand Prairie Texas was in the middle of a huge tract of land between Dallas and Ft. Worth. I could see how that area would be perfect for cows, it seemed every bit the big open range. I Googled that phone number that had come in with his call; it was a landline assigned to Mark Smith and the red arrow went to an exact location on the Lyndon B. Johnson Highway that said Farm Bureau. Probably an office there, maybe a dormitory arrangement for people caring for the animals and doing research. I concluded that it might not be such a glamorous life after all; this location would not be one of choice. (Didn't look like there would be a Neiman-Marcus for miles!)

At least I had been able to successfully verify both his location and phone. I felt good about that and I slept well that night.

I looked forward to each new day. I eagerly got out of bed, took Oliver on a long walk and couldn't wait to return to my office and start chatting with Mark again. I looked forward to learning all that I could about him and sharing some of my information with him as well. I was careful to not reveal too many personal things too soon, and purposefully never mentioned anything to suggest any information about my finances. I was also careful never to mention anything about the countries and continents I had visited; I feared it might leave an impression of my circumstances that he might greatly exaggerate. I also left out many personal details. I did share that family and friends were always extremely important to me and I was a very social creature and would hope to find that quality in a partner. Our chats were fun, flattering, often exciting, and lasted easily for two hours or more per session. However chatting online really can't replace the immediate gratification of hearing someone's voice, or being with them in person. I found that I loved listening to him and the interesting lilt in his voice, and preferred that a thousand times more than sitting and chatting.

"Hi sweetie. How are you today and have you taken your walk yet?" He would ask nearly every morning. Some mornings he would call to tell me either that he had time before work to chat online, or that he didn't have much time to talk on the phone but "I just wanted you to know I am thinking about you and let's set up a time to chat online." I looked forward each morning to that little bit and with every day the little bit grew larger.

"Mark, I am still thinking about you and New York. Do you ever go back there to visit or do you have a place there?"

"No, he started, I have a place, it's near Central Park. When I take a holiday I go there. I have my friend there. But-um-umm I'm welcome to visit him as often as I like."

"Where does he live?" I was curious about the friend, and how close they might be.

"He lives right near Central Park," he said, and then "I'm welcome to stay with him any time as long as I like."

I was a bit confused about who owned what and stayed where but it didn't seem totally important at this stage and besides, he was in Grand Prairie now and whenever he got a vacation he said he would probably hit the big city and stay near Central Park in either his place or that of his friend. Seemed like a good deal. Central Park was a respectable neighborhood.

(I could enjoy spending time in Central Park, with him.)

There would always be time to find out more, always another call, and always another chat. So far so good.

Later that evening the phone awakened me.

"Hi, Babe, I just wanted to hear your lovely voice one more time before you went to sleep." Mark's voice sounded like he was smiling.

"Hi Mark, that was good of you. Did you have a good day?"

"Kind of tiring, there are hundreds of animals to inoculate and it takes a long time."

I'm not sure which one of many questions I hit him with first but he enjoyed answering them and did so with a continued smile in his voice. We did talk for a good amount of time and then he recognized my need for sleep so he signed off with his plans to go join some friends and colleagues for dinner somewhere.

"It's a Chinese restaurant near by, and we get

together and talk about everything. I think tonight I'll tell them about you."

"I'd like to be a fly on the wall for that conversation," I said, wishing I could just be there in person. Visions of Mark at the dinner table surrounded by assorted wine glasses like in the photo he sent me. Probably his friends had taken that photo. Yummy.

"What do you mean?" He asked, not understanding my expression of the fly on the wall.

"It's really not important, doesn't matter," I said, "I'm really glad you called."

"But-um-um I just wanted to tell you I hope you sleep well, babe, and dream good dreams of me."

With that he left the call to join his friends for Chinese food and left me to turn out the light and obliviously follow up on his suggestion, to dream about him.

# Revelation

Somewhere near six in the morning I sat straight up in bed and my jaw dropped open. Oliver, suspicious that we were perhaps leaving early for a road trip or other equally exciting adventure, sprang to attention, licked my chin and tried to encourage me to move to another position besides the seated one. I could not. I was frozen in thought.

I had spent the night allowing my mind to wander in and around Mark, his voice, his speech, his —

"That's it, Oliver!" "I know exactly what it is. Why didn't I think of it until now? It's the Bahamas!"

Clearly Oliver was not as thrilled with the news as I, and even less impressed that I was now leaping out of bed barefoot, with no sneakers in hand, heading quickly toward the computer down the hall as opposed to the front door. Not an encouraging sign for having his morning needs taken care of and his routine visit with his pals. This morning he would have to wait.

My fingers flew over the keyboard telling Mark that I now knew what had been in the back of my mind for some time now and it was only this morning that I had finally been able to put my finger on it.

"Your little expressions, a few idioms thrown about, your slight accent and specifically the phrase "but-um-um" was not foreign to me. I had just been so absorbed with the newness of all of this I had over-looked it."

Yet I recognized exactly that Mark Smith had roots somewhere in the Bahamas. How interesting.

"There I was," I wrote him, "living all those years in the Caribbean and you were in the Bahamas not too far away. Do you suppose that's how your profile came into my inbox?" I still pondered the problem of distance.

"Do you think that the computer just linked the Caribbean and the Bahamas as a 'match' and decided to put us together?"

I'm sure Mark would respond to my pronounce-ment and questions later.

I thought it odd in the beginning that someone from New York could end up in the inbox of someone living in southwest Florida. The whole idea is to enable the couples to meet, be able to have a date of sorts, and go from there. Something about a 50 mile maximum radius from each person's location.

I was excited about my discovery and so happy to have put those dots together.

"I have heard that accent before," I had told him a few times, but had let it slip.

"It had always seemed a bit odd that there was this accent from somewhere, and uncharacteristically for me, I never picked up on it until later."

Maybe I had been out of the Caribbean too long. I had rarely failed to detect one island dialect from the other. The Bahamian sound is fairly specific when you hear it . . . this Mark Smith surely had turned my head sideways, inside and out for me to miss this. I was clearly absorbed with this man.

Well, no matter, I would now indulge Oliver with his morning walk while I asked myself over and over how I could have overlooked something so major as the Bahamas.

"Oliver, how the hell did I miss that accent earlier? That's not up to my standard at all."

He was focused on finding his friends and a place to relieve himself so he left me to figure it out on my own. *He's probably thinking his usual dog thoughts: if you can't eat it or screw it you . . . well he found his patch of grass!* I decided to wait and see what Mark would say about my revelation.

My answer came in a mid morning email from him.

"Sweetie, you must be utterly brilliant and clever." (So I was right!). He went on with his explanation.

"My dad went to the Bahamas years ago and was hoping to find a wife, and then he met my mum. They had two kids and that's where I grew up. I'm not sure how you picked up on it but you are right. . . ."

The rest of his email trailed off into questions about how I had spent my night, and had I taken the dog on his walk yet, questions that would imply he was trying to learn and familiarize himself with my daily habits. He mentioned, before closing, that we could chat later online. I made some notes on a few questions I would have for him regarding my new discovery and kept an eye out for the chat hour to arrive. As always, I looked forward to communicating with him.

"I left the Bahamas in high school and finished in New York and went to college in New York. I later went to vet school at the Royal Veterinary College, the University of London, and later did some practice there."

That sounded very interesting to me but I was still hung up on getting more information about his time in the Bahamas. I knew a bit more about that region than I did about veterinary schools, particularly ones overseas.

"What island in the Bahamas?" I added into the chat. He seemed at first to not respond to that question so I rattled off a few names as an example:

"Cat Island, Marsh Harbor, Eleuthera maybe?"

"Rock Sound" was his response.

I questioned that further, he went on to name a few spots in that region but I was unfamiliar with the names, though I had found Rock Sound and it seemed to be a harbor area. It left me thinking that his dad must have been amazing to travel there from somewhere else to find a wife-unless that trip was an accident. It is such a small area with an even smaller population base. I would presume the pickings would be slim. Nevertheless it had happened, according to him.

"I had a sister that died in childhood, and my dad was my mentor. Everything I learned, I learned from my dad. It was good to be a man of principle and integrity and to treat your wife with great love and care."

Certainly good qualities to have learned, I agreed.

"I certainly can't find fault with that. It is good you learned some good life lessons from your dad.

You must have been very close."

A few pieces of information here and there each time we chatted helped to create a complete picture of the man, and I found him to be increasingly more interesting.

Later that night an email came from him.

. . ."I can't escape the thought of you. Even in my dreams you are there. It is not fair you are not with me. To dream a dream is to waken your inner self. Your wants, your desires, your passions, are given life. Have a wonderful night rest.

Mark"

He had added two emoticons of red roses beside his name.

My head was slowly turning.

A week passed quickly. Many emails, chats and phone calls later we both had settled into a cozy routine of talking at least twice a day and sending and receiving about three or four emails a day. Many of those were either a short paragraph or a single line, but it is the thought that counts and I knew he was thinking about me at least as much as I was thinking about him. His tone was always upbeat, his voice was always smiling, his words were always warm and well chosen. Little by little, day by day, he was getting more of my attention.

The phone got me awake before seven. Mark was smiling the minute I groggily answered.

"Hello."

"Good morning Sweetie, I couldn't wait to talk to

you and hear your voice so I decided to call now and hope it isn't too early. Are you awake?'

"Just barely, but it's good to hear you nevertheless. What are you doing at this early hour?'

"I was just talking to a friend of mine overseas, he and I are pretty close from when I lived and worked there and his mum just passed, so that got me awake I guess, when he called me."

"Oh, that's too bad," I said; feeling sad for his friend's loss of his mother but it was difficult to summon real sympathy for him, or anyone else for that matter, at seven in the morning.

"Do you need to do anything about that or was just talking with him enough."

"No, we just had a long talk, you know, and since I was awake I really wanted to hear your voice. I miss you, babe, I wish I could be there to meet you, you know?'"Oh, believe me, I do know. I have thought the same thing for a while now."

"I'm about finished with this project in Texas, I was hoping we could get together when that's over. What do you think?'

"I think it's a wonderful idea, and certainly about time that we got a chance to meet one another. When do you think you will finish?"

"I don't think it will be too much longer now. I'll keep you posted as I go along and we'll plan on me coming straight there to see you, is that Okay?"

"Oh, I think it's a great idea. We can sort out the details later but it is important and I'm so eager to meet you. Good, it's settled then, now I'm excited and it's not even eight o'clock yet!"

"I really miss you, Babe, I want to meet you really bad."

"Yeah, I know, I miss you too and it sounds like we will meet very soon."

"I have to go now Sweetie, but you know I'll always call you later after work if that's okay?"

"Okay, you know I will look forward to hearing from you, whenever you have the time."

Of course it would be okay. It would be more than okay and I would spend the rest of the day trying to concentrate on what tasks and chores were necessary, counting the time until I would hear from him again. He was becoming my whole day and this was becoming fun. A far cry from the earlier cast of characters, my cereal box gang. I deserved something good and someone good in my life. Imagine my good fortune of meeting this great guy so early on in this process and to know how well this was all working out.

It was a warm and fuzzy feeling.

# London Calling

It had been a while since Delsey and I had enjoyed a lunch date and there was so much to share at this point. Sam, although he worked near by, was unable to join us as he often did.

"Delsey, you look fabulous. Matching shoes and bag, where do you find these things? You always look marvelous."

"A few things here, a few things there, she said, but truly I have never seen *you* look happier or more alive than you do now. This Mark Smith is evidently good for you, you look fantastic!"

"I feel like a different person. You know how hard I tried to get over Vicente, and to finally feel something for someone else that is this interesting and seems to care about me, it's wonderful. He seems totally in tune with me and he's someone that I could see myself sharing a life with. It's exciting. He just seems right for me and everything is going along so well; except I'm not too sure about this latest bit of news."

"What news, what's going on?"

"Oh golly, a few days ago he called me that he had just received an urgent message to go to the UK to bid on some work there."

"What kind of work was that?"

"He was called by some entity in London, probably through his Royal Veterinary College, to bid on some work to be done somewhere. He wasn't sure where, but he would find out when he got there."

"Well, now," she said, "that sounds like it could be interesting; so when does he leave?" Delsey always wanted facts to be nailed down. I was the same way except trying to nail down Mark was a bit like nailing jello to the wall.

"He's already gone. He told me he had to get there quickly. They were having some work study program to get people acquainted with the project, then he was to work with a team of people that he would assemble and come up with a scope of work, then bid on that. Whoever wins the contract gets sent to wherever it is for some time."

"Good grief, so he's there already, in England?"

"Yes, and I've heard from him several times. He gave me a number where I can reach him and he seems fine but he's in class most of the day studying and learning."

"That's amazing, I wonder what the project is?"

"I'm sure we'll know soon enough. The thing that's disturbing is that right before he left Texas he told me he was leaving for Manchester, England from Miami, and when I asked about that route he said he had to collect a colleague who lives in Miami somewhere; they have evidently worked together in the past and would be traveling to England to work together on the project."

"I hope it's a male colleague," Delsey's mind went to the same place mine had.

"I already asked him that but my bigger question is why he didn't allow even a half hour before his flight to England, so I could have gone to Miami to meet him, even briefly, before his flight took off. At least I could have met him and we would have known if there was real chemistry between us going forward or not. What a colossal waste." I was irritated. I was also disappointed and hurt . . . maybe a bit angry.

"Well it sounds like he left in such a scramble he probably didn't have time." Delsey was trying to give him the benefit.

". . . Or, maybe," I said, "he didn't give it any thought, which is worse."

I had managed to think this through as though the shoe was on my foot now instead of his, and I would have made every effort to meet before leaving for an extended period. I couldn't understand why this didn't happen.

"How's your St.Croix salad today?" We ordered it almost every time we chose this restaurant. The name and ingredients made it an obvious choice for us, having both lived there for many years.

"It's just fine" I said, and then added, "How are your crab cakes? I think I'll try those next time. They look delicious." She nodded her head to denote pleasure.

"So what do you think of all this rushing business to get to England?" I asked Delsey.

"I wish you'd had a chance to meet him first, but

he left in a hurry. He gave you his number over there; have you called it yet?"

"Of course I have, and some British sounding woman with an appropriately charming British accent is the voice on the answering machine, or the voicemail in the hotel. He mentioned having gone to the service at the cathedral with friends, and there really is a lovely cathedral in Manchester. I have no reason to believe otherwise."

"Could I have the check please?" Delsey was intent on writing off our lunch as a business expense. I suppose she felt responsible for getting me involved in this romance business.

"Thanks, Delsey. You need not take me to lunch today, but thank you. I guess time will tell about this London business. I believe that as it appears to be a preeminent veterinary college in Europe, it undoubtedly gets requests from all sorts of institutions and agencies and probably even governments, and time will tell how this works. He used to live there while he was in school and I'm sure that he told me he worked there for a few years afterward. I know he told me that he and his wife lived there while they were married, and his daughter was born there."

"Well, we'll know in time; and in the meantime you look fabulous, regardless of where he is or what he's doing you look *t e r r i f f i c*, and I give Mark full credit for your transformation!"

"Thank you, thanks to Mark, and thanks again for lunch. I'll keep you posted."

That night a lengthy email arrived from Mark.

*. . . now that I have found you, I have no intention of losing you, not now, not ever . . .*

I was very special to him and he was already looking forward to this bidding process being over so he could take a vacation and come straight to me for a little holiday together.

"Now that he had found me, he had no intention of losing me. . . ." I liked the sound of that. It went a long way toward helping me over my non-trip to the Miami airport to meet him in person.

# "Falling in Love with Love. . ."

"Mark, I love chatting with you but I went to look up something on your profile to talk to you about and there is no profile. What happened?"

"I took it down," he said. "The minute you 'winked' at me and the first time I heard your sweet voice and we started talking on the phone and chatting, I knew you were the woman for me. There was no point in leaving my profile up there."

"That makes little sense to me. You just posted it not too long ago and why not be absolutely certain about me or anyone else before you take it down?" It made no sense to me at all.

"I am certain. I don't want to bother with anyone else. I want to concentrate all my effort on you and making you happy. Is that okay with you?" Mark always had a proper response.

"Oh, it's okay with me. I haven't heard anyone say that in a very long time; if ever. I just hope you know what you're doing, Mark, and that you're very certain."

"Babe, I have never been more certain of anything in my life. You're the one for me. I just know these things. I feel it. I hope you feel it too."

If the truth be known I was definitely feeling something, I just wasn't prepared to identify exactly what it

was, at least not at this time. Another thing, having
gone through all the silliness of that damned TV station
and program, and signing up for this stuff, I sure as hell
wasn't going to dismantle my profile so soon. It didn't
make sense to me. What if Mark Smith was not 'the
one.' I still hadn't met him. No, I would be content to
wait a bit.

"Mark, I'm not sure exactly what I'm feeling right
now, but it's something, and I'm not prepared to take
my profile down just yet"

"It's okay, Babe, hopefully you will want to soon
enough."

The matter was dropped. At least for this day.

These chats with Mark in England became more difficult for us both. Somehow, between his pressing work
and study schedule, the five hour time difference and
the intermittently long instant messaging, he managed
to squeeze in a few phone calls to me.

"I couldn't concentrate too well today," he started.
"I was thinking about you all day and hoping you
weren't being scooped up by someone on that dating
site. I'm just not comfortable being so far away and
knowing you're still out there and available."

"Don't you worry about that, you just go do what
you went there to do, and make sure you learn what
you're supposed to learn so you can be brilliant when
the time comes."

I tried to be reassuring. I truly wasn't interested in
visiting the site to 'find' anyone else. I felt connected to
Mark. I would follow this as far as it could go, but it

made no sense to dismantle my profile just yet. Besides, the whole "looking online" process was horribly time consuming and I was already tired of it. My profile could sit idle for a while.

"I'm working with my own team and we each have our own specialty so we're trying to propose ways in which we would solve various problems if they came up. I've been told my team is doing very well, so I guess we have as good a chance as anyone else." He sounded upbeat and optimistic.

"I want to know everything about you, Mark. Everything. I like to think of it as my own brand of school. We take care of questions and answers first and then finally we can move on to 'recess.'"

"Oh, I love recess, let's get there quickly, so bring on the questions, Babe."

So I brought on many additional questions about his life, education, his work, the answers were all about the same as before. I was still struggling to remember all the details in that profile that had first attracted me, the one he had dismantled. He said he had written it himself. He had used words to describe himself as comely, charming, capable, captivating, clever, cunning, competent, and I was trying to remember if there were other attributes or adjectives that began with another letter. The 'c' words all seemed to fit so far. Even though he had not used many of those words in his conversations with me.

"I'm an honest man, Babe, a man of integrity. I don't have or want any drama in my life. You told me you liked your calm and easy life and I don't want to ruin that for you; I want to add to your life not take away from it. I want to give you everything you want and need, and add value to your life. I have found you, my sweetheart, and I don't intend to lose you. I'll not be going back to Texas when this is over, I have no reason to be there. I want to be with you. I can go back to New York and find a place for us there."

"Mark, that sounds lovely but how can you just walk away from Texas? You were living there!"

"I was working there, Babe; the work is done and I'm here now; when this is finished I'll have no need to go back to Texas. I'll be wherever you are."

"So you were only living there because you were working there"? I seemed to be always going back to pick up something, like a dropped stitch on a piece of knitting.

"Babe, don't be confused. Yes, I was working there on diseases in livestock and their offspring, so yeah, living there. It's done, so I can go wherever I want to go now, and I want to go wherever you are. Unless you prefer we think about moving to New York."

"Well, for me, New York is not an option. It's hideously expensive, especially the Central Park area, and I moved to Florida to be with my family and friends and don't intend to move now. The tax base in Florida would probably be favorable for you and your line of work, as I presume you can find work anywhere at any time."

"Yes, I can, and I will certainly think about Florida . . . are you suggesting I move in with you?" His smile broke into a soft chuckle and I heard the anticipation and expectation in his voice.

"Maybe we can talk about it *after* we meet."

I thought that was reasonable for now. I had not really given that any thought until now, but In any developing relationship the possibility exists that someone moves in somewhere with someone. I guess I wasn't prepared for the suddenness of this.

A quick chuckle and a shift of subject got me off the hook this time, but the question certainly was worth revisiting, and probably soon.

It was now early March and I had known Dr. Mark Smith and been attracted to him for every minute since, February — well Valentine's Day.

He had just been discussing moving in together. Other things we discussed seemed totally reasonable, although maybe faster than some would think acceptable. There really aren't rules for matters of the heart. One thinks this, the other thinks that, but only the two who are involved share the opinion that ultimately matters. My friends have always been supportive of me, and my interests, and while many seemed interested in this particular man I know there were large looming questions about his truthfulness. Questions for which I also needed answers.

I had been thinking a lot about my own feelings. Certainly they were growing. I wasn't prepared to use the L word just yet but my feelings were very real. I was taken with the fact that Mark was everything that I had been looking for and was certainly attentive to me, but of greater interest was his ability to relate to me. He could read me well, and he knew what to say to make things better. Either he was a very old soul or he was just a simple man, as he described himself, who was totally in tune with a woman who, he said was, 'the one.' The fact that he might be a highly skilled professional in matters of the heart never entered my mind.

The days passed. During the brief phone conversations between his work and study we did come to an understanding about finally meeting. I thought it best if we choose a neutral location. What seemed acceptable to both of us was New York City.

"The Plaza Hotel is known for its cozy Champagne Bar. I've never been there but it seems to be a perfect place, and a romantic spot for a first meeting. What do you think, Mark? You know New York better than I."

"Oh it's a great place, a fine hotel and I will take care of all the expenses, of course."

"I would insist on separate rooms, and we could enjoy all the sights and sounds of New York and get to know each other in an area familiar to you." I thought it would be the perfect solution. Neutral territory.

That afternoon a wonderful email arrived. Mark was writing quite eloquently about our relationship having fallen into place under God's direction. He had no doubts about our relationship or he would have stopped communicating a while ago.

"I recognize that I am able to relate to you on a higher level than I ever have before with anyone, and I have never felt like this before. I am not interested in looks, or money. Although both might be beneficial, they really are not important. Your looks blow me away, you take my breath away. I want a love that will give me a reason to breathe. I am looking for a soulmate. I am not a perfect man, but I am prepared to be as perfect as I can be, for you. I am a responsible man, a principled man and have much love to give. I have experienced deep feelings stirring inside of me and believe I have fallen in love with you."

I read his email over at least three times. I had turned to butter. He had used the L word. I was not yet prepared to go there but here it was. The telephone interrupted what would have been my fourth re read of his declarative email.

"Good morning, sweetheart, I'm so happy to catch you before you head out for your walk. My colleagues all tell me that I'm in the best position to be awarded this contract based on our exam and our team efforts, and today we find out what happens. Either way it's good news. I'll either win the award or I'll be coming straight to you."

"Oh Mark that's wonderful news. I hope you're successful but I'd be lying if I didn't tell you part of me hopes you don't win this, so you'll be coming back here. I want to meet you so badly."

"I know, sweetheart, I want to meet you as well but one day soon we will be together talking about this. Bye for now. I have to run and get ready for our big meeting. I'll call when I know anything at all. I miss you, Babe, Bye."

I was visualizing all the activity surrounding him. The colleagues, the studying, getting together at the end of day in the cafes, the exams, and the final wait for the award announcement. In the midst of all that was going on with him, I suddenly felt very alone; yet he reminded me daily that I was always in his thoughts. Not meeting him before he went to the UK was still upsetting to me. I felt that I was falling in love with a man that was unavailable. We were separated by many miles, and many hours and had not ever met. What a strange circumstance. Why then did I miss him so very much? I had no answer, only the constant ache from wanting to be with him.

"I've great good news!" He was nearly shouting but I could hear the excitement in his voice. "I've been awarded the contract for the second category and I've been posted to a third world country . . ."

"Where?" . . . I interrupted anxiously.

"Malaysia, Babe, and have been appointed to the Department of Veterinary Service under the Ministry of Agriculture and Agra-Industry. The contract period is for three weeks." My heart dropped. Malaysia was further than I had anticipated.

"That's great news indeed, Mark, I'm happy for you. I can tell you're excited." I was happy for him but feeling a bit like I had when he left suddenly for the UK without meeting me first. Here I go again.

"There's a cocktail party later in honor of the winners and I will call the minute I get back to the hotel to tell you about it."

"I'm sorry not to be there with you. Cocktail parties are my specialty!" I really was glad for him but would love to have been going to that party, meeting his colleagues and spending time with Mark.

"This is the last one ever of these that I'll be doing

without you, Babe, so you'll have plenty of time to be by my side for formal functions."

I wanted to believe that, but for now, I was sorry to be missing out on everything. It would have been a fun occasion. I poured myself a glass of wine, snuggled back into the sofa and started humming along to the old Rodgers and Hart tune on the radio, the lyrics of which seemed oddly ironic: "Falling in Love with Love is Falling for Make Believe . . ." and wishing I was by his side at that party right now. I managed to separate the lyrics from the tune in my mind, and hummed a bit longer.

Mark sent an email that night explaining it had been a late event, there was plenty of vodka and all kinds of wine, cheese, dinner, speeches, toasts, and people, and he had wished for me to have been there by his side.

"The contract is only for three weeks but it will be a positive thing for our future together, babe, and I'm going to miss you dearly."

I was a bit surprised at the reference to 'our' future together but I liked the sound of that.

"I will be in touch with you daily and I will likely be traveling by the weekend after my documents are in order.

He mentioned he had a surprise for me and would send that by another email later.

" . . . *God will not be happy with me if I don't tell you how much I miss you, and long to be with you, as distance never really separates two hearts that care, for*

*our memories span the miles, and in seconds we are*
*there. But whenever I start feeling sad because I miss*
*you, I remind myself how lucky I am to have someone*
*so special like you to miss. You are my dream come*
*true, Babe.*
     *With love*
     *Mark* . . . Followed as always with the two red
rose emoticons.

The lovely thoughts in this closing email were still
registering along with the earlier reference to all of this
being an advantage for our future together and my
being by his side for all future events and ceremonies.

His inability to rhyme was momentarily excused.

I called Delsey. I hadn't spoken to her yet today
and she always called me in the morning to get an
update on the romance; she had joyfully taken full
responsibility for its orchestration.

"It's very clear to me, and should be to you," she
said, "that Mark is going to want to be married to you.
He's not going to be the kind of man to drag you
around as his 'girlfriend' to all these formal functions. If
I were you I'd get used to the idea very quickly. I see this
as a part of your future with this man."

Clearly I wasn't prepared for that remark or that
eventuality. I had already made my own prognostica-
tions years ago:

• I was never moving to Florida.
• I was never getting another dog.
• I would absolutely never get married again.

I was still holding on to the latter with a vice-like grip. Marriage? Never!

Oliver, now ensconced in a pillowed, privileged existence in Florida, had been pleased he had made the cut!

"Hang on Delsey, there's a new message in my email inbox from Mark."

As it came through I was not believing my eyes.

"Oh my God Delsey — wait 'till you hear this." and I began to read the contents of the document that Mark had won and was now sending me. Now I understood why he was so excited and how he tied this into our future. It was awarded to Dr. Mark Smith in the amount of One million, Two hundred and fifty-thousand dollars (USD) and the terms of the contract just as he said; all properly stamped, sealed, and signed by the Minister of Agriculture (the name totally unpronounceable) for Malaysia. I was in shock. All of that money for a three week contract to work on Avian Flu virus for the government of Malaysia. Good grief! The following document was simply a copy of his flight itinerary on Emirates airways. Evidently he was being routed from Manchester through Dubai into Kuala Lumpur. He wanted me to be comfortable knowing that and that when he arrived in Kuala Lumpur he would buy a cell phone in the airport and phone me the minute he reached the hotel. I made a copy of both documents and stared at them in disbelief. Holy crap!

Delsey and I were both in shock trying to figure out if

*all* these types of contracts were worth this kind of money. That's serious money for a flock of birds in my mind; sick birds at that.

(I wonder how much *healthy* birds are worth?)

It seemed safe to say that at least this veterinarian was financially secure.

No wonder he could afford to cover all the expenses at the Plaza in New York. This contract could buy many bottles of champagne!

One more time I questioned how all this had happened so quickly. It seemed almost too good to be true. How could it happen that a man I had not yet met, had managed to turn my head so quickly, stir feelings within me that I had kept buried for years; talk about building a future — and now he'd just tossed over a million bucks into the mix, not that money mattered, and had me concentrating on the L word with every passing day?

Yet, it had happened. Here he was, on his way to Kuala Lumpur half way around the world, now twelve hours ahead of my time zone, and all I could think of was how much I would miss him. I still had no idea how that had happened. I also had not told him I was fairly sure I might be falling in love with him.

# Malay, Melée

$\mathcal{M}$alay is a term used for a person of Malaysian descent from Malaysia or Indonesia; it is also the official language of Malaysia. Melée is also a Caribbean term used to describe a fracas, social upheaval, or chaos. While the two words are pronounced the same way, they carry a totally different meaning, depending on which location you're in. I could only hope they were not interchangeable where Mark and I were concerned.

The Caribbean, both beautiful and seductive, owns a reputation for a lifestyle that goes beyond relaxed. That implies that there is a lack of structure, which often gives way to chaos. This general deterioration of a more structured system is fondly referred to as melée. On a social level the term is often used to indicate a breakdown of communication between friends, business associates or lovers. Somewhere, someone is stirring a pot, and the intended outcome is again, melée. Melée can be bordering on morally corrupt, or it can be genuinely entertaining, like a carnival sideshow. Confusion can grip an island and become part of the way people do business and communicate. Melée, or mayhem, is what the West Indian people thrive on. Whether it was through participation, or in stories being passed down, creating melée was a national pastime.

I wondered about the similarity of these words and the meaning each carried. Which one of these words would I be involved with as it pertained to Mark Smith? Confusion and moral corruption or carnival side show?

Only time would tell.

Mark Smith described his local living arrangements in Kuala Lumpur as an adequate suite, which he simply said was okay. He had cable, the internet, a bathtub, access to a gym and was only a short walk to the area where all the birds were kept. He shared his cell phone number with me and would call after making his first inspection of the birds.

"They are in such a terrible condition," he reported later. "They are so sick, some have already died. We need to get them vaccinated as fast as we can before we lose more of them. The conditions are deplorable and I'm glad you're not here to see it. It would break your heart."

"What's the delay with the vaccine? I thought that was the first thing you would do when you got there." It seemed a logical question for me to ask and I was quite sure that's what he had told me was first on his agenda.

"In reality," he said, "I have had to make some adjustments with this labor force. The regular Malaysian workers are fairly good but they want twice as much money so I have talked this over with the Malaysian boss and I will have to find some Indian laborers."

"I assume you mean like East Indians?" It already appeared to look like a debacle was in the making.

"Yes, exactly," Mark replied. "They work for much less money and although they are not as good or as skilled, they can still get the job done with supervision. That's what I'm here to do — supervise them —so it should be fine."

Suddenly nothing seemed fine. Vaccine was late arriving, birds were in deplorable condition and now there was a problem with the indigenous labor force wanting too much money. The Indian work force was not as skilled but would work for less money. That spelled trouble to me.

"Are you sure this is going to work out, Mark?" I had great reservations over this compounded problem.

We switched from the more expensive cell phone call back to the chat for the remainder of our conversation, and exchanges of loving thoughts, warm wishes and loving expressions of missing each other. It usually would take thirty minutes for those warm and fuzzy conversations, and online chatting certainly made that more affordable.

Each day brought a more gloomy report than the day before.

"The birds' condition is worsening." Mark's report was gloomy and fraught with discouragement.

"The vaccine has still not arrived and is now nearly a week late. I don't understand it at all."

"Is there any good news at all?" I wanted something upbeat to hang on to.

"The workers have been mostly exchanged and

the teaching process is underway. I am also initiating proper procedures for handling the sick and dying birds."

"How do you feel that's going?"

"They seem to be getting it, and I hope that the workers are absorbing all the information about taking proper sanitary precautions to safeguard their own health as well as that of the birds."

"Mark, you need to take care of yourself as well as these workers. It won't do for you to get sick."

"Don't worry, babe, I'm taking care. It's really hot and humid here and the place where the birds are kept is unreal; but I'm taking good care."

It just all seemed to be very unpleasant, at best. The major task at hand seemed to be to keep the workers healthy enough to separate and then to vaccinate the birds. Time seemed to be of the essence. Still no sign of the vaccine.

Early into the third week, three of the more capable workers were hospitalized with the very flu virus they were working to eradicate. Evidently there had been a breach in proper procedures which had sent these workers to the hospital. Mark assured me he had taken proper precautions for himself. He was, after all, in the health care business and would be fine. The workers were being attended to daily, and in a short time they would be fine as well and back to work. More delays for the project but so far nothing life altering. When sharing this recent development with a dear friend I had been reminded that according to the World Health

Organization there had been no known outbreaks of Avian Flu among humans in recent years. That news was comforting, at least these workers didn't have the full blown flu but probably some weaker strain that would only set them back a few days.

"The vaccine finally arrived, Babe, it's at the port right now." Mark sounded relieved, "So I'll be off to pick that up. It's a huge relief and the workers are getting antsy because there's so little they can do to keep the healthy ones alive without that vaccine."

He went on to assure me that the arrival of this vaccine made this a very special day and it was bringing us closer to being together as the project finished. In spite of the several week set back and the sick workers I guess it didn't look like a bad day after all.

I was enjoying the phone call and feeling better about the news of the vaccine arrival. Mark's voice turned harsh, lower in pitch with no softness to it at all. Not the same voice I had known or loved to hear.

"I have tried to explain the situation to you, Babe, in all the emails I sent but you didn't seem to understand me at all; you were ignoring me."

He was right. I had no intention or interest in getting involved with his bird and labor issues. So I had changed the subject always to something more pleasant, or something having to do with little scraps of trivia from my own very comfortable stress-free day. Any discussion of money always waved a red flag for me. I decided it was time to tell him why.

"My former husband, back when we were living on the island, developed the fine art of trying to get me to pay for everything, from a multi-thousand dollar macadam driveway to replacing an oven, because nesting mice that had moved inside for the winter had chosen to live in my oven, and eaten through the wiring. That ruined me for men *and* money."

*There you have it in a nutshell, so don't mention it again.*

There were always good reasons to ask, and better reasons to ignore. I didn't want to be asked so I chose to ignore. It was a bad sign.

It was close to midnight in Florida, I was very tired, and that is unfortunately when it came.

The phone call. It was loud and obtrusive like a large elephant in the corner of the room trumpeting the question that would no longer be ignored.

"Babe, will you please loan me the four thousand dollars for the vaccine? You know I can pay you back when this job is done."

"Whoa, whoa . . ." I jumped in immediately, and just as immediately he continued.

"I can hand deliver you the cash when we meet in New York. You know the terms of the contract, I can more than double what you loan me and in a few weeks I will meet with you, my sweetheart, and hand you the money in the Plaza hotel!"

There it was. I got to my feet and walked around in circles, squeezing the phone as if it was his neck, while silently contemplating my answer which was doing a slow roll over in my head. I had an avalanche of emotions coming at me, everything from rage, disappointment, love, anger, despair, hurt — and then without any warning, I found words spewing from my mouth. My voice was loud, full of rage, and very specific.

"Mark, there simply is no fucking way I am going to lend you four thousand dollars to get some stupid vaccine off the dock because of the shortfall on the estimated amount for taxes on landing it there! All for a bunch of birds!"

I was enraged. This had hit my angry spot head on. I raised my voice to an even higher decibel and continued to interrupt his "but, umms."

"That's your god damned problem and I'm sure as hell not going to help you solve it. You had weeks in England to work on this problem and to make sure all your financial planning for this project was in order and so this is *your* fault, you asshole, *you* created this fucking mess, *you* can god damned well solve it for yourself."

"Babe, just wait, oh God, please just calm down, there's no need to scream at me . . ."

"There's every reason in the world to scream at you, you bastard!"

"I really had no idea, Babe, absolutely no idea this would happen and that they would charge extra for taxes to offload that vaccine."

"How the hell could you NOT know that, dammit, it is your JOB to know it!"

"Gay, it was coming from Germany and I really had no idea there would be extra involved because of that."

"You're an ass, Mark- whoever- you- are- Smith. You claim to be a vet, you claim to move all over the world doing projects, and you had to know the vaccine was in Germany, you had to know you would have to pay a fee, you had to have built that into your cost. What the hell's the matter with you? Did you think someone would hand deliver vaccine to you for free?"

"You have to believe me, Babe." He was becoming emotional, but he had nothing on me!

"Don't 'babe' me. This sucks and I'm furious. This is *not* my problem and don't make it my problem. You told me you do this for a living! You're supposed to be a professional. *You* bid on this job not me, *you're* getting paid for this job, not me, what the *fuck* did you call me for anyway! I'M DONE! DONE!"

The line went dead.

I was shaking with rage. How dare he! I walked around the room some more, still squeezing tightly to the dead phone. I felt like a tea kettle that had run out of water but was still producing a good amount of steam.

Some time passed, but I had not been able to get back to sleep.

"Hello, Babe," Mark was quieter now and with a softer voice. "Please don't hang up on me, please, please." He was interrupted several times by my rather professional use of four letter words, adjectives, verbs, nouns, all used interchangeably and not necessarily nicely, before he had a chance to cut in and finish his thought.

"I am going to be able to reimburse you for every penny of what you lend me and will even double it! You have seen the size of the contract I will be getting, the minute this project is over. It's all for us, Babe, for our future together, and it's just a loan; I will pay you back, you know I will. I love you so much and this is for us and it's only a loan. I can even have you get the money into the hands of the dock master and supervisor, if you prefer, just to prove it has nothing to do with me, but we need the vaccine, Babe."

"Where do you get this 'we' shit, Mark? I don't need any of this crap. None of it, you tell those fuckers at the dock to go fuck themselves. I have no intention of paying them anything — or you either, for that matter." I was grappling with all my earlier emotions but anger was still winning.

"I am so disappointed in you for even asking. On top of all that I wrote you about what a history I've had with that sort of thing, now you pull shit like this."

"I already told the supervisor and dock master that I've been trying to get in touch with my wife and she would be able to take care of this when I could reach her. . . ."

"You told them WHAT! What 'WIFE?' I was certain my neighbors could hear every word through the concrete block walls, even at two in the morning, even two blocks away. I was red in the face and fuming like a chimney. "The audacity of you, you shit head, what the fuck would you tell them that for?"

"Because I love you and this is for us and . . ."

"There is nothing for us. Nothing. You ruined everything. If you loved me this wouldn't be happening."

"I knew if it was you over here I would have done everything possible to get help to you so you wouldn't suffer. The birds are dying, Babe."

"It's not me over there. I wouldn't be caught dead over there and I told you, I don't give a good damn about your shitty birds!"

"Don't you think I hate asking a woman I love for anything at all, let alone asking her for money?"

"No. You have proven you are perfectly willing and capable of asking me for money and countless others too, maybe."

"It is killing me to ask you this. Oh, Babe, you make me so ashamed! I'm afraid that the workers will lose confidence in me and that would be a disaster."

"Guess what, I don't give a damn about your workers either. It's *your* problem. You deserve to lose their confidence. You've already lost mine!"

"I can't jeopardize this project, Babe, and you'll get every cent back plus double when this is over."

I never answered him. I never made a sound. I hung up the phone again, still trembling, and did the only thing I could think to do. I cried. Cried out of total disappointment and utter frustration, and anger. It made little sense that he couldn't take money from his project — but was told he could not get access to that until the project was completed. The credit card issue was my obvious next suggestion but was told that he had mentioned to me back in England that there was a hold on his credit card until he got back to New York and went personally to the bank to handle that issue. I vaguely remembered that conversation but dismissed it. It seemed a bit absurd and it had nothing to do with anything. I couldn't understand how anyone who was a professional could ever leave the country in such a hurry that he'd failed to make sure his financial information was in order before such a trip. Maybe I hadn't heard him correctly then, or maybe I hadn't wanted to. I had no answers, only questions. I would have to try to sleep on this, but I couldn't. I stared at the ceiling as if it was a blackboard and the teacher would soon come in with a big piece of chalk and write the solution to the problem. No teacher appeared.

Sleep never came.

A week earlier I had submitted a request to a private investigator who's name I had come across in New York City. It had been suggested to me and I thought it wouldn't hurt. If Mark Smith had lived there or visited often at any time it seemed a PI might have a way of tracking him down. I had heard back only that so far there was nothing found on him. No name, no street address, no phone, no anything. Empty data base. Nothing in Texas. Nothing anywhere.

I was never a bird fancier. I loved dogs. Soft, furry, sweet, intelligent, faithful, interactive dogs. Money for a flock of birds, sick ones at that? Hard to wrap my head around that.

I was adrift in a sea of thoughts. I had phoned Delsey first thing the next day to discuss this four thousand dollar fiasco. I needed someone to talk to. This was not how any of this was to have played out.

I had invested months into this relationship. I had desperately wanted it to work. I believed we had a good chance at happiness. Why was it so difficult to see the betrayal? There was the cerebral part of me that knew this was outlandishly wrong, and stupid from the beginning. There was my intuition, that never failing female foolproof intuition. Rule number one: never send money overseas to people you haven't really even met. In spite of everything that happened I wanted to believe the best in him. All my life I wanted to give people a second chance even when they may not have deserved or earned it.

Delsey and I talked for a long time and we each concluded that we wholeheartedly believed, in spite of everything, all the evidence to the contrary, we believed that he was the real deal. We believed that he did indeed love me as he had been telling me for months, and that we would be together after this whole project ended. Two hopeless consummate romantics, Delsey and I, trying to persuade each other to be a bit less pragmatic. I was the one who had been part of the conversations, chats, phone calls and lovingly romantic sessions with him leading up to this. I thought I was in love with him. He said he was in love with me. Somehow, while it would make no sense to the rest of the world, it made some small amount of sense to me, that the best thing to do was to take a chance. What if there was a shred of truth to this? What if he really was in a huge mess beyond his immediate control? What was the worst thing that could happen?

"Delsey, don't you think it might be worth the risk

of four thousand dollars to find out if he's telling the truth?"

"I can see your point but what if you find out he's just a con artist?"

"I think I have to know one way or the other. He's either a con man extraordinaire at worst, or at best he's just a wonderful man who loves me and is in a huge jam, in a dreadful place, and about to make enough money to pay his sweetheart back doubly well?"

"I see your point, Gay. It's a tough one. I think he loves you, but you're the one who's been in this with him. You're the only one who can know what to do. You know it's a risk." I have never been a gambler. The odds never stack well in my favor. This was a bad gamble. In the end, the risk and the love won the day.

"I am so proud of you, Babe, I just picked up the money from Western Union. This is a great thing you've done and I'll not forget you or forget what you've done for me. I can't wait to finish this project so I can get this all paid back to you and double, just the minute I get to New York." Then perhaps a deflection of his own, "We need to discuss whether you want to live in New York or not. I was looking for a place for us to live when I get back, but we haven't talked about it yet; what are your thoughts, Babe?"

*Right now you really don't want to know my thoughts.* I would reserve those for now.

I had done what I said I would never do. I knew exactly why. I took that risk. It was over and done with. It was like eating that big piece of chocolate when you know you shouldn't, and unless bulimia is involved, there's no getting that chocolate back. There might be consequences but it seemed the right thing to do at the moment. I rationalized that four thousand dollars, while not an insignificant amount of money, is what I might have spent on myself during the year for a number of things which I probably did not need or want, like food, clothes, travel, hair cuts. I still saw my actions as incredibly stupid maybe, but fortunately for me, not fatal.

The decision had been made. The hand had been played. I would have to live with the consequences and wait and see.

Mark had called very late the following night and was happy to be able to get to work and so happy I committed to helping him. He apologized profusely for having put me in that position. He ultimately calmed me down from my profane verbal fire storm of the previous night. He whispered sweet things to me on the phone and it confirmed that, for now, my decision had been the right one.

I had never had 'makeup sex' quite like this but there was one thing certain, Mark Smith gave good phone.

# Bienvenidas Costa Rica y Nicaragua

$\mathcal{I}$t seemed to me that I had been immersed in this romance to the exclusion of everything else. When the 'everything else' included Oliver, it was time to step back and give him the attention he deserved. He and I had become a pet therapy team the previous summer and his superb temperament made him the perfect candidate for serving the needs of others. He is bright, very social, and extraordinarily intuitive. His eye contact is unwavering which makes him able to diagnose situations and quickly adjust to each circumstance. No challenge seems too large for him.

A favorite situation for him had always been going into schools during Animal Kindness week or curling up next to a child on the library floor and listening, with two soft non-judgmental ears, to story after story. The libraries provide the fuzzy soft mats that kids nap on in pre-school; the children pick a mat and then choose a book to read. When they return, book in hand, most often Oliver is curled on their mat waiting for the story to begin. The kids decide whether to choose sharing the mat with him or sitting close by so they can twirl his soft ears around their small fingers as they falteringly sound out each word. He listens obligingly, without judgement, and is then rewarded by the child choosing yet another book that he has probably also heard a hundred times. Every now and then the child will pause, and turn the book around to let Oliver look at the pictures. He may not be good at deciphering the content of the picture, but he appears to be interested by resting his muzzle on a child's knee and looking directly into their eyes. He is brilliant! There's also the added bonus of being served a tasty Frosty Paws treat by Mother Goose herself, posing as library staff, and getting to visit with his other four legged pals. Doggie Tales is always a rewarding outing.

I tried to schedule as many libraries and schools as I could during these weeks immediately following the incident about sending the money to Mark. I tried to occupy my time with something productive and helpful. It helped take my mind off my own problems while perhaps making life a little easier for others. The result of children learning to read, or enjoying reading much more because of a dog, made the whole experience a win-win for everybody.

I had already planned to take a week off to visit dear friends who had been instrumental in finding my home in Florida. They were the kind of warm outgoing people that I was taken with at first meeting. They had lived in the community just a few houses away so we had seen each other frequently, and the more I saw them the more I liked them.

Jack and Jennie moved from the neighborhood a few years after I moved in. I was so sorry to see them go. It's harder to keep in touch when people move away. That was true at least until they chose to winter in the lovely warm area of Costa Rica. We had spoken of my visiting them there and using my time share exchange. I left the end of March for Guanacaste on the Pacific coast of Costa Rica.

Oliver would be staying with my daughter and family and be quite content until my return. I had arranged a cell phone that would allow me to contact Mark in Malaysia if I chose, however I had opted to back far away from Dr. Mark Smith for a while. Mainly I was going to use the time to visit with my friends, share their wisdom, relax, become a tourist, and sort through all the recent online events.

Clearing customs was a snap, and I rolled my suitcase out to the street and rushed into the outstretched hugs of Jack and Jennie who were enthusiastically running toward me. How good to see them again. They were a sight for sore eyes, and took me first to the time share unit I would be renting . . . or not. It was on the third floor, there was only a view by day of the sea. Because the sun would be streaming into the window the shade would have to be drawn, no point on being on the third floor looking out at roof tops. Finally we got it all sorted out with a unit closer to the pool on the ground floor, and then after signing papers, and getting keys, we drove into town to have some local fish and beer at their favorite local spot, Papaguayo's. Jennie couldn't wait to jump into a conversation.

"I have to tell you, you look fantastic, have you had a face lift or something?" Jennie had been a nurse and always interested in the body, but what was more important was her connection with her spiritual side that enabled her to see inside a person. That's why I found her to be such a fascinating friend from the start.

"No, Jennie, no face lift. Same old face as always but there's been a lot going on in my life since I saw you last."

The conversation shifted to Mark, and everything that had been going on. (All but the part about my having gone to Western Union with four thousand dollars to send to him, before I had ever met him in person! Few, including myself, would know why I had done that, and I certainly wasn't proud of it.) Jack seemed like he had already heard enough of this romantic tale and ordered another round of local beer for us. Taking that hint, I turned the conversation to a discussion of possible activities and sightseeing excursions over the next few days. I could always talk with Jennie tomorrow.

Mark did not reach me until the following morning but was very happy that phone service was available. Malaysia to Costa Rica was just far enough apart to add an additional three hours to the usual twelve which would prove to be difficult, inconvenient, and very expensive.

"How are you, Babe? I'm so glad I can get through to you. I was worried when I didn't hear from you right away. Are you okay?"

"Yes, Mark, I'm fine. Just busy enjoying myself with my friends."

I didn't feel like talking to him, which felt odd, but it seemed right to maintain my distance from him so I ended the conversation.

"I have to go now. I'm meeting them up at the pool area."

"Okay, Babe, I won't keep you. I just miss hearing your voice and I love you and hope you stay well. Have a good time. I'll call you again."

"Good bye, Mark." I was in a hurry, I could have been a bit less abrupt, I simply didn't feel trusting. I wasn't sure he deserved it.

The enormous condo pool was inviting, situated in the midst of a lush tropical setting with large trees and flowers everywhere and the scent of jasmine hanging heavy in the air. It made me feel like I was back on St. Croix. Jennie and I had so many things to catch up on. We spoke of all the friends we shared in Florida, the highlights of their lives; then there was Mark Smith.

I explained how we had met, his background, what he was doing now and where, and she was fascinated. On a spiritual level she thought many things were very interesting about him, and hoped to learn more about him over time. Mark's second phone call of the day to me interrupted us and, judging by the time, it would be our last before night set in. Jennie and I would have to finish our talk later.

"I'm worried about you, Babe. You seemed a little quiet last time I called and I hope everything is all right with you. Is it?"

"Yes, Mark I'm fine." It was thoughtful of him to be concerned but I was still in no mood to speak to him.

Sending that signal to him for the second time, I disconnected the phone.

The condo I was using had not worked out. It proved to be too far from Jack and Jennie's place and therefore very inconvenient to visit back and forth. Jennie insisted I move into their guest room for the remaining few days and so it was settled.

Later that afternoon as my hosts and I were enjoying our first round of cocktails Jack took advantage of the limited time he would have access to the internet. I had remembered only too well how the power supply fluctuates in the Third World countries, so he took advantage of the electricity being on to try to solve my continuing and nagging question of who was Dr. Mark Roger Smith.

"This is the damnedest assignment, Gay. I've never had a problem finding any information on anyone but this Mark Smith doesn't seem to exist anywhere!"

When Jack also came up empty, we made another round of drinks and turned our thoughts to grilling vegetables to accompany our fish for dinner.

Jennie was a great cook and loved fresh vegetables. She was willing to take the necessary time to prepare anything, she just loved being in the kitchen, and I admired and appreciated her effort. While she was chopping and mashing, I took advantage of the still available electricity to email Mark, telling him again that I really was still bothered by him asking me for money for his job:

"Surely you've figured out that I am beyond annoyed by you asking for money. I won't get over that any time soon. I particularly don't understand how you could ask, after all the information I gave you, how I felt about that."

I felt I had reached a turning point. Did I have a premonition that another shoe would fall? I was losing interest in this problematic labor force and their ignorance of the terms of contracts and I was losing interest in Mark Smith. I was hurt, disillusioned and becoming more distrustful by the day. I sensed that somehow there might be another "issue" and I really didn't want that to surface. I sent the email off and then I uncharacteristically turned off my cell phone, allowing my email to be received, read, and remembered. I was looking forward to going off alone to Nicaragua for the day and would be getting up very early in the morning to catch my ride, not to return until nearly midnight.

Nicaragua was having a very dry spring. As the shared touring van drove through the countryside, heading toward the border from Costa Rica, I began scanning the landscape for signs of the lovely Senepol cattle I used to see back on St. Croix. That breed was particularly drought resistant and very massive. They had a docile look about them and a deep red mahogany color. I remember that some of them had been shipped to Costa Rica years ago. It had been an awkward looking sight to see them being loaded into the cargo hold of the plane. I thought it would be fun to see one of them now in their new surroundings but I saw no evidence of any Senepol here. The thought of cows encouraged my first and fleeting thought of the large animal vet in over twelve hours. I didn't now believe he had ever been in Texas, or even in Malaysia.

We had been driving for a few hours and finally made our first stop for breakfast; and just in the nick of time for my ninety-minute bladder. Breakfast *typico* was rice and beans, plantains, fruits, breads of all kinds and strong Costa Rican coffee. Nourished and ready to face the world we returned to the van and prepared to visit the National Park of Masaya, an active volcano area, dangerous because if it chose to erupt while we were there viewing it, we would have little chance to escape unharmed.

*(Great, just what I need, to be burned alive by a hot molten lava flow chasing me in a foreign country. Nobody will ever find me, and the camera will have melted, and I will die out here, alone!)*

The last group of tourists that tried to outrun the lava flow met their demise as the very vehicle being used for their escape melted, faster than they could drive it back down the road away from the spewing lava ash. I snapped a few quick photos of the area and of the van, and of the people who were sharing the experience with me. Fortunately we were among the lucky, but we were all looking out our windows and encouraging the driver to use great haste to get us out of there.

The tour of the market in the capitol and main town of Grenada and the boat ride on Lake Nicaragua were relaxing and danger free. The climb to the top of the church tower provided a magnificent view of the whole of Grenada. Nicaragua had one major problem that would seem insurmountable and that was the border crossing between it and Costa Rica. Lines of over one hundred or often twice that many, snaked a trail of sixteen wheelers waiting to pass through customs, single file. This section is well known for its drug issues. Drugs being picked up at the Panama canal are carried by truck through to Nicaragua then on up Highway One as far north as Mexico. Truckers who were greasing palms of officials would create another long line, exiting the truck only to show papers, passports, other documents and get back in the truck and get into the next long line to cross the border in single file. I couldn't imagine driving this route every day or even once a year. It was an incomprehensibly asinine process and to a van full of good natured tourists it simply defied all comprehension.

It had been an interesting outing, with only one single thought of Mark Smith. My bladder and I were glad to finally reach the condo in Costa Rica by midnight.

# Exhaustion

*J* was sitting all alone in the dark with only the light from the computer screen, reading the subject of Mark's email sent while I was in Nicaragua. *"Come back to me Sweetheart."*

I felt a bit sad, and curious to read how he had never cried for a woman until now. Yet I was not sad enough to let go of the anger and betrayal.

*"I've been so worried and upset about you, afraid something awful had happened to you. I had no idea how to reach you or where you were."*

I know I had mentioned my day trip to Nicaragua, I know I had mentioned I would be leaving early and I know I had told him the cell service in that country was not compatible with Nicaragua. His email continued.

*"I'm just afraid, Babe, afraid of losing you, afraid something bad happened to you, and afraid that my plight in Malaysia is getting to you."*

Well, he certainly was right about that one. It was more than getting to me.

I had no idea why all this was going on in my life now. I really did not want drama or turmoil. I simply wanted to love a man, and have that love returned. Was that asking too much? I had believed that was how this had started out, but it certainly was not how it was ending up. Maybe this love affair was only designed to be a 'lust' affair for two months. That seemed pointless. I had more questions than answers. Mark continued to mention on several occasions that he was still having problems with the Indian workers and had been in a constant battle with their boss regarding the need to push for closure on the contract so they could all be paid. They did not understand the terms of the contract. Mark's frustration had grown, and I was left with this niggling feeling in the back of my mind that what he wanted, or what he intended to ask for, would be my help in paying off these workers. Time would tell.

"... *miss you my love,*" *his email continued,* "*please don't keep me in tears without hearing from you, see what you've done to me my darling, I can't handle this falling in love with you because you have captured my whole heart. I'm sick from this and can't continue, I really need to hear from you. Are you okay and where are you now? Did you lose your phone? It's on forwarded calls. I do not understand what is happening, Sweetheart I really need to hear from you. Please give me a call I need to hear your voice. I love you darling and I miss you.*"
*Your soul mate*
*Mark*"

I sent off a brief, if not terse, reply.

"I'm okay. My trip was very long, and I am struggling with issues of who you are, and I am only trying to protect myself. I am having trouble verifying anything about you. On top of that I was beyond upset about your conversations regarding money matters for the workers."

I was totally exhausted and couldn't face a phone call to him.

"I really don't want to talk to you." That covered just about everything.

It was late to begin thinking about this now, but I felt it was beyond time that I think about protecting myself from this probable outcome. I thought I was stronger than I was, when really I was sensitive and vulnerable. In spite of everything, I was still weak kneed just thinking about him. I had wanted this relationship to be real and the direction it was taking was terribly distressing. My emotions had been raw for some time and I asked myself repeatedly why I ever had to fall for a man like this. I asked myself that over and over. I could have continued to enjoy my quiet, calm and oh-so-predictable life without Mark Smith, or any other man. Having no man was better than having the wrong man. The universe could be cruel; he had been put in my path, hadn't he?

The following day was a good day for hanging by the pool. Enough activity and long hours in Nicaragua had tired me out, along with the additional stress of being unsure who Mark really was, and why, after everything, I was still hooked on him. It was exhausting. I had not spoken to him in three days and was missing that terribly, yet I knew it was best to avoid him as I struggled with all the same old questions that I had from the beginning, including the main one of how to verify this man. It was becoming harder and harder to believe in any of this at this point. I had accepted the lack of verifiable information as good news, when it was just the opposite.

Jack and Jennie had each taken turns on the Google search for information regarding his home ownership, his veterinary degree from London, living relatives, whether he owned a car, and it was all a dead end. There was no information. Anywhere. I tried to find any publications he may have had attributed to him for research projects in a given area and again there was nothing. Yet here he was, big as life in the middle of my life, and there were nagging loose ends that could not be tied. My common sense was evidently on holiday while I was enjoying the feeling of being in love. It was a frustrating time and I was terribly torn between lack of verifiable information, and my love for someone who may have been a ghost on paper, but was very real to me.

Cocktail hour gave me an excuse to summon my courage and place a call to Mark. I had given it some thought over the past few days and in spite of all the holes in his history, I had managed again to overlook them in favor of a revelation of my own.

"Mark, all my life I have tried to fix people. My friends, family, problems, relationships, anything. I simply tried to fix the universe. Some, like my ex-husband, were beyond fixing, and yet I continued to try. I had asked the universe for a man with a specific list of qualities. I had *assumed* he would be a whole, normal, adult functioning man who had control of his emotions, and now what?"

"I'm not sure I understand all of this, but I'm trying." Mark managed.

"It means, Mark, that I'm trying to figure out how to react to a man who I know nothing about." *(I also can't find out anything about you period, and that's not a good thing but I'm not going to tell you about that right now.)*

His soft chuckle and lack of comment seemed to be a sign of acceptance of my comments, though I was sure he did not understand what I had said.

"I guess now, I will have to settle for you as you are and time will tell me the rest that I need to know. That will take some getting used to."

Mark was a good listener but seemed a bit beyond confused at my outpouring. I babbled on for forty-five expensive minutes, and never once asked him to verify anything to me. Nothing from nothing still left nothing, so had I given up on that process? He listened, and uttered sweet nothings into my ear, no doubt relieved he would have no questions to answer, and everything seemed fine. I never realized that my effort to explain *my* need to fix everything in the past, had undoubtedly played into his need to have me do just that. In my lengthy account to him I neglected to mention the most important piece, which was my inability to find out anything about him, anywhere.

My final night in Costa Rica was spent at the Pacifico Club in Guanacaste. I was taking Jack and Jennie for dinner and we were to join some of their friends first for cocktails on the seaside patio. A man playing some favorite reggae tunes on the patio made me feel a bit nostalgic for another time, another man in another place who was very real. It would be hard for me to give up the fact that Mark Smith was likely not who he told me he was. I was, after all, a hopeless romantic, and a large part of me was wanting this to work out. There was less and less to hold on to, yet somehow I was clinging to anything I could.

The trip had been a good experience for me and brought me closer to realizing more about myself, my needs and, with the help and support of good friends, I was slowly putting the puzzle pieces together.

# The Deepest Blue

*O*liver had been overjoyed to see me when I returned. With wagging tail, spinning and nearly levitating off the ground from sheer excitement, and assaulting me with many kisses, I knew that this indeed was unconditional love at its best. Why would any sane woman think she could come close to receiving this much devotion from a man! The question would go unanswered.

During my week's stay in Central America, a local Florida high school had experienced a rash of tragedies. Several student suicides and auto fatalities involving both students and teachers had occurred within a short span of time. It was a grim time for that community. The Pet Therapy teams had been called in to provide help and comfort and I had made it home just in time to help respond to the call.

I approached the school auditorium with trepidation. I wished I had not dozed off during my college psychology classes, I might have felt better prepared for what lay ahead.

"Oliver, buddy, I don't know what's in store for us today but this is going to be very hard for you, not to mention me. You just do what you have to do and I'll follow your lead."

I pushed open the double doors and sucked in my breath, hoping that Oliver at least was prepared. I really did not know how to perform this daunting task that faced me. Our training had not specifically included dealing with this type of tragedy. The beauty of the Pet Therapy Partner team is that at least one member is in charge and knows exactly what to do, the other member goes along at the other end of the leash. (That would be me). Oliver recognized he was in charge today and pulled me swiftly along, sensing his mission was at hand. The thing that struck me was the role each of the dogs assumed that morning. No one assigned them anything, they individually seemed to know who would accomplish what task. One mellow chocolate Lab chose a spot on the floor, planted himself in a reclining position and waited for the students to come to him. A black Portuguese Water dog took up a position in the back of the room and was doing tricks. Bowing, shaking hands, fetching after tossed toys, and some students sought that clownish amusement to comfort them. Oliver pulled me toward the door, and stopped there. He had decided upon being the official greeter. Each student who entered the room got a tail wag, kisses, and a smiling face with intense eyes that delivered his message.

*"I care about you, I know you are in pain, and I am here to help you get through this, come to me."*

It was magic. One by one each student would lean down to rub his head, touch his fur, stroke his long ears, and mostly just smile back at him. Others chose to curl up next to him once he sat. Some buried their heads next to his, communicating or transferring their pain. Oliver never flinched because he understood. One student who had been a particularly close friend to a deceased student wrapped her arms around Oliver's neck, rested her cheek against his head and allowed her tears to flow openly, maybe for the first time. As I glanced around that room my eyes welled with tears. There was so much pain, yet I marveled at the ability of each one of those dogs to know, in their own way, how to lessen the misery of others in such a warm and wonderful way. I was immensely proud of the depth of love and understanding packed into my thirty pound dog, and his ability to know instinctively how to help these students and teachers so profoundly.

"Oliver," I said choking back tears, "I am very proud of you, you are the best dog in the whole wide world and I love you."

I was the silent partner at the end of the leash that day but Oliver, in his very intuitive and caring way, had taught me a great lesson about kindness, empathy and the simplicity of love.

Driving home from that emotionally wrenching experience it was hard to avoid recognizing the inevitable fragility and short duration of one's life. I was not getting younger and for me, wasting any time, like the time that had been abruptly stolen from these young students, was pointless. By the time my car swung into the driveway I knew what I was going to do.

I had spent a week reflecting, dreaming, and ultimately realizing that in spite of the drama and my introspective self observations, it remained likely that Dr. Mark Smith was undoubtedly *not* the man I thought he was. I still had feelings for him — that would take some time to get over — but those feelings were now more about my disappointment, and my need to move on as best I could. Finishing what I had started, I put my profile back up on the dating site. It had been long enough. Odd, thinking about it now, but only the week before leaving for Costa Rica, I had totally emptied out my second closet in the bedroom. I had believed, or hoped, that Mark would soon be leaving Malaysia and when he came to visit, at least he would have a place to hang his clothes. It was amusing to me how that had seemed like a good idea at the time. A good idea until my buddy Dave, who had come to assist with switching shelves and moving around some partitions to create more space, asked the big question.

"Exactly why am I fixing this closet for you?" My answer was simple, but evidently too silly for him as his reply was swift:

"Holy shit," he blurted out, you're rearranging this whole closet to create space for a guy you haven't even *met* yet?"

I thought it was amusing then but the wisdom and the humor of his question resonated for weeks thereafter. Little by little I started to put my own clothes back into that closet along with some additional stuff.

Still, allowing the profile to become inactive had been a suggestion Mark Smith had made from the very first week. He was concerned, insecure about my remaining on the site. I had not removed the profile, only let it sit there unattended to — a correction that took no time at all to get it up and running again. Surely this time I would have a better experience. Always the optimist.

The first fellow was Tom. Tom lived south of me and emailed me his interest in meeting me, and after a few phone calls he invited me to dinner. We chose a mutually convenient restaurant half way between our two locations and I set out for a pleasant evening with a new man. Someone other than Mark Smith.

Tom was local, lived forty-five minutes away, was semi-retired from the real estate business, divorced and looking for a partner. (This is what should have happened from the beginning, I thought.)

Tom was tall, with white hair, a mustache, good manners and nicely dressed as he rose to greet me and escort me to our cozy booth.

"You are every bit as lovely as your picture," he said, "I'm Tom, I'm so glad to meet you at last. Please, have a seat." He motioned me into the booth.

When the talking began I was quickly overwhelmed.

"So tell me about yourself," he started. Then, before I could make an opening comment, he picked up the ball and ran with it, the full fifty yards down the field. Like it was a contest.

There was simply no room for me to jump in at any part of his monologue. He was rapidly fluent on every subject and never stopped to catch a breath. Each time I interjected a "but" or a "what do you . . ." into the conversation he would grab it away and go on about himself. I had never experienced anything quite like this before.

*I know how he has become so successful in real estate: he simply talked his clients to the point of sale so they would buy just to shut him up.*

The waiter was a pleasant, attentive fellow. He made several stops at the table to check on the order, advise about the specials, refill the water glasses, and bring fresh glasses of chardonnay. Had I known then what I had learned by the end of the evening about old Tom, I would have ordered a double vodka. Maybe a triple! (In hindsight I should have excused myself immediately and simply left the restaurant, taking the waiter with me!) At the end of the evening I had heard Tom's entire life's story. He was so tragically boring I could remember none of it. He had zero interest in what my story might have been, nor did he give me an opportunity to jump in with any other story. He paid the bill and with his hand on my elbow, escorted me toward the front door. I jumped into my car as quickly and politely as I possibly could.

"Thank you for the lovely dinner Tom, it was . . ." and sure enough Tom grabbed even that brief thank you speech away.

"I thought it went very well" he had interrupted, "and I look forward to seeing you again."

*How the hell do you think it went well? You're totally boring and not even if you were the last man on earth would I want to see you again.*

He announced he would be giving me a hug good

night and contacting me the next day. (Who does that?) It sounded like an orchestration of benign intent, until the hug became a kiss and was not to my liking, nor was it returned. The next day Tom sent me an email that was beyond bazaar.

"I enjoyed the evening very much. You are beautiful, and an amazing woman and I enjoyed you immensely."

*What was it you enjoyed? You never gave me a chance to complete a sentence. How the hell would you know that I'm amazing?*

*What's really amazing is that I didn't excuse myself between the salad and the entree and leave your ass in the booth!* Sadly, his email continued:

"I have developed a strong sense for making love and I want to share that with you. I want you to come down here and spend three days with me in my home, so I can prove to you how much I enjoyed the evening!"

*Yuck!*

If that wasn't rapture enough, he enclosed three photos of his house as bait.

*Do you think the photos of your pool and condo are supposed to seal the deal? Not even if it was the friggin' Taj Mahal!*

I was appalled at this approach and wondered how he ever got the idea he even *liked* me, having spent no time talking *with* me. I had probably spent more time responding to the waiter's questions about menu options than I did with the guy who paid the tab! It was blatantly obvious that old Tom didn't give a rat's ass about me, he just wanted to get laid. Back to my old familiar option.

Delete.

My profile had been only up for one day but it had not been a productive start. (This had a familiar ring to it.)

Mike was the next to contact me. An older gentleman who sent a brief email or two of introduction and wanted to buy me an iced tea in the local town. I suspected immediately that he would not be a big spender, but with time and place decided, I slid into the booth across the table from him and sipped slowly and cautiously on my tea. Mike seemed pleased that the tea refills were free, which confirmed my initial suspicion, and then asked a rash of questions about me, and I about him. He began his story first.

"I was divorced after many years of marriage and she got the house and most everything else.

*He's bitter — she got the house.*

"I relocated here because of some family and with only a few bucks in my pocket."

*First it was the free refill on the iced tea, then wife gets the house, now he's living with family in the area because he has money issues. I sure don't want to get the tab here, and I think he is figuring he's better off single. I'm beginning to know I am.*

What's his game, I wondered.

At the end of what felt suspiciously like a job interview, he asked his final question.

"Do you like sex?" I tried to conceal my amusement and amazement at the question, but I acknowledged him simply and directly.

"I find sex is an important part of any relationship. I think it's a strange question to ask." *I'm having a hard time visualizing having sex with you anyway, like it or not.*

"I asked because so far, most of the women don't like sex or aren't interested in it any longer."

*Do you think it might have something to do with your approach? Or maybe the glass of iced tea you use for foreplay?*

"Well, that's unfortunate for them, that has never been one of *my* problems — however I have to have very strong feelings for the man to even contemplate sex."

*And, not only do I not have strong feelings for you, but a glass of iced tea does nothing to change my mind.*

He must have interpreted what I said as a sign of optimism, and what he hoped would be forthcoming. He took my hand and walked me to my car, and asked me out for the following evening. He appeared eager. I appeared bored but polite. I couldn't see this going anywhere, but I was working on trust and willing to give this one final try.

The date was confirmed by a phone call — which involved my asking him for enough pertinent information so the community security would allow him through the gate.

"No serial killers or rapists allowed in the community," I had told him. He seemed only mildly amused.

I realized later that my yielding to his insistence to

drive me to the movie as opposed to my meeting him there, was not a good idea. Something else I had read *not* to do. However, I had already met him and he was old enough to seem perfectly harmless. He picked me up at the house, which was not my idea, but he was determined, and it seemed important to him. He had argued that it was the proper thing to do. I rationalized that a man his age could be of little harm, and would most assuredly try to make a good first impression, to insure a chance at a second impression.

We had to make one small stop on the way to the movie to pick up his decongestant at the drug store, after I had asked if perhaps his sniffling indicated he had a cold. (I dismissed the thought of drug abuse.) He shoved his purchase into his pocket after slipping something in his mouth and we headed on to the movie. Somewhere toward the end of the action film he stopped sniffling, the "decongestant" must have kicked in, and he grabbed my hand, lifted the arm of the seat so it would be more comfortable, as he unmistakably tried to grind my hand into his crotch. *Really? Who does that on a first date, and at your age?*

I was not able to tell if his recent purchase at the drugstore might have been of the small blue variety, but I was suspicious now. I couldn't get out of the movie fast enough, strategizing how to get back home. I didn't wish to bring up the subject of his crotch certainly, for fear of another uprising, or simply being dumped out on the highway. We continued on with an exchange of only stiff conversation. If that was all that was stiff between us I was very much in luck. Back in the driveway I thanked him for the movie and was prepared to send him on home. I knew from his profile he didn't drink so when he snatched the house key from me to unlock the front door, and asked if I could get him a cola or something for his ride home, I gave it little thought.

He accepted the cola, sat down on the sofa, and leaned in toward me for a kiss.

*Not this again, what in the world is wrong with these guys?*

I don't think old men want to be bogged down in a relationship, they're online only looking for sex. This was not for me. If old Mike thought he could get what he wanted by the expenditure of only one ice tea with free refill and a movie, well I guess he figured it was worth a try. I was strongly pushing him back away from me when I spotted Oliver, flying toward us with lightening speed from across the room, and he landed full stop on Mike's lap! (How do dogs know things?) This "decongestant" buzz kill was delivered by an Australian Labradoodle!

*Good work Oliver, you're the best!*

Off went old Mike, promising to contact me again.

*Really? I think not.*

Thankful he was gone, I began mulling over the events of the evening. Thank God for my perceptive and faithful Oliver.

"Oliver, you are really the best dog in the world, and tonight you earned yourself a biscuit!"

One morning an unexpected email arrived:

"*The Deepest Blue*

*As I gaze into the deepest blue*
*So strong is your will to love and be true*
*Your soul I see; your heart, I feel*
*As I gaze into the deepest blue*

*You're afraid to love due to your past*
*So broken is your heart vexed and aghast*
*Heaven you pray; please make the pain go*
*away*

*Storms continue to rage as I gaze into the*
*deepest blue*

*To mask the pain; you say being alone is true*
*However, your heart yearns to love again all*
*anew*
*You try to stifle love; love wants to soar up*
*above*
*As I gaze into the deepest blue*

*Let your heart feel love again*
*For living in the past only brings disdain*
*Embrace love, and let love live once more*
*As your eyes reveal love, in the deepest blue*

*Mark*

It surely wasn't Keats, or Shelley but I could wager
it sure as hell wasn't Mark Smith either.

It had been several months since there had been any contact with Mark Smith. I was getting over him and I was glad. Yet true to his sense of the romantic, when I had received similar poems in the past, it had always been when he was attempting to sweeten me up for a financial solicitation. This poem followed true to form.

"I need and want to leave this horrible country so desperately, to be with you and prove my love to you. I am tired, and confused, and I just want to be with the woman I love. The workers have gone back to work and things are slowly being completed; I am sure to be joining you soon. I still love you, Babe, and we have a bond together. Remember?"

*Well, no, I don't remember any bond that you didn't already break.*

More poems arrived. One which made little sense to our situation but the photo inserted at the beginning of the poem was unmistakably clear. Two gold wedding bands intertwined. It did nothing for me.

There had been a time I would gladly have twirled around like Oliver doing his happy dance, upon receiving such a poem or picture from him. That was not what I felt like doing now. I was over him. I did not hear anything more from Mark after his poetic attempts for many days, but I went looking for similar poems online later that day, and found the same one. The author was anonymous.

"Babe, you won't believe what happened. I'm so sorry to tell you but I was robbed!" The email went on to describe how two thugs had attacked him on the street at night as he returned from the industry and presumably were expecting him to be carrying large amounts of cash, so they hit him over the head and stole his briefcase at gunpoint. He had not been seriously injured but they had made off with some important documents, cash, and his cell phone. Which was his explanation for not having called.

His saga of bad luck just seemed to continue. My interest had ceased.

". . .*If the sky were made of paper and the ocean my inkwell I still couldn't describe how much I love you.*" Mark wrote.

Lovely thought but it could only mean he was in need of a new cell phone and there was the matter of the missing cash. It added up to another untimely delay in leaving Malaysia. I was not interested, nor did I care.

"I hope the police can retrieve my briefcase so I can get my phone back. I miss the sound of your voice. I am so sick of being in this country and all I can think about is getting out of here and coming straight back to you."

Several more days without Mark contacting me. I didn't mind at all. I figured his phone had not been replaced but that didn't explain why his email was not arriving, until he offered that the power fluctuation in that country forced him to abandon the old computer in the hotel and go to a nearby cafe, and with his current health problem, that had been ill advised. No suggestion as to what had happened to his laptop, nor did I care. Curiosity took over and I responded to one email to ask what health problem he had developed.

"My pressure was high and they told me that I needed total bed rest. I am so weak and tired and just want to come home. I am so sorry ever to have asked the woman I love for anything and I hope to not be a bother to you any longer, I only want to be with the woman I love and not to die in Kuala Lumpur!"

*Bravo! Bravo! You could have won the Oscar had not Colin Firth played such a brilliant King of England with a real medical problem, you jerk!*

On a hunch, and for the hell of it, I called the Royal Chulani Hotel in Kuala Lumpur where he had been told by the police to relocate after the robbery. The hotel had no such guest as Dr. Mark Smith registered at the hotel. Surprise, surprise!

I had also contacted the FBI with full details of the situation on Dr. Mark R. Smith from the beginning to date, and was told there was little they could do, their hands were full with large (multi million dollar) threats and scams and unfortunately unless my life had been threatened there was little they could do. If or when my life was threatened I could contact my local police department. If the FBI was telling me they were over-whelmed with the numbers of these scam artists I could only imagine how many there must be out there. There had to be a way to catch these guys. I needed to find one.

*Part Two*

# Bajan Pepperpot

Spring had come to Florida and insanity had come to Malaysia. I had not heard from Mark since my return from Costa Rica and when I did it was clear what he had been up to. He sent me an instant message chat.

"Do you have any equity?" I knew where this was headed and responded negatively.

"Do you have a HELOC?" He persisted.

Initially I was not familiar with that term but wanted to play along. A bit of research informed me he was referring to a home equity line of credit.

"No, I don't believe so Mark, why do you ask?"

I simply was stupefied how any of this information could possibly be of use to him. Naïveté is one of my less endearing qualities but this unfolded as quite a sinister plan of his.

"I did some work for a company overseas some time ago and they still owe me some money from that job."

"That seems odd that they would still owe you money for a completed job under contract, Mark."

"Well, it's the truth and I have worked out a plan so that I would ask that company to send the money they owe me from the job and send it to you. You could deposit the money in your account and wait for me to send you instructions when to make checks payable, and to whom to make them payable."

*You really have worked out quite a plan for yourself this time!*

"Mark, there is something very wrong with that plan. I have something on the stove, I can't deal with this right now."

That scheme would help him pay his way out of Malaysia and then he could come straight to me. Only problem with his plan is that according to a member of the FBI that I contacted about this character, this is money laundering, pure and simple. His advice to me was to get as far away from this immediately. Period, full stop. I dropped it like a hot potato and fired Mark off an email that explained what the FBI had said, and even suggested that if he had come up with this scheme on his own, then shame on him. If others had helped him cook this up then he was keeping very bad company and I encouraged him to get as far away from them as possible.

That was my way of telling him I had spoken to the FBI about him *and* his scheme. It should also have sent a message that I was on to him. (Now that I knew for certain that Mark Smith was broken, I hoped that my having told Mark that I had contacted the FBI wasn't my attempt to try to fix him!) In the back of my mind I began trying to figure out a way to trap him at his own game. He never responded to that email, he never spoke of the money laundering scheme again, nor did he ever reference that email.

I know Mark got the message. I didn't hear from him for another few weeks, then, characteristically, I began receiving more love poems. He wanted something. This would be interesting.

One poem in particular, spoke of wanting a new beginning.

*"I wanted a new reason for living, and no words could express that you are the only woman for me, my reason for being and you are my life, and my soulmate, and, is there anything you could do to assist me in leaving the country?"*

That last request of course had no rhyme, unless it would be *crime*!

It was difficult to think of Dr. Mark Smith as a person other than the one I originally thought he was, the fine looking man in his profile. Clearly there was another person. It was hurtful and infuriating. I was tempted to drag it out only long enough to trap him, though that would be very risky. It had been a stressful time but a phone call from my friend Cathy in Barbados presented me with the perfect opportunity to put a plan together.

"Gay, how are things going? I haven't heard from you in a while. I was hoping you might have some time to come visit me. I can't get away from here for another few months but would love it if you could find the time to come here for a while. Any chance you could?

"Let me think about it, check on flights and I'll get back to you. It would be fun and we have lots to talk about. I think I could use a friend about now."

One of my favorite Caribbean spots had always been Barbados, for a number of reasons. It was a lovely island with magnificent beaches, the cuisine there was outstanding, there were things to do that were fun, and I had a very good friend who lived there.

Cathy was a woman whom I had met originally some fifteen years ago on St. Croix. We were both attending a tourism conference. Sam was also attending the same conference and introduced us. We became instant friends. We had many things in common, socially and professionally, and chatted throughout the conference and agreed to visit each other as time allowed.

Cathy had recently been to Florida on business, and so it seemed now was the perfect time for me to make a visit to Barbados. I had spoken to Cathy in the very beginning about the 'love affair' with Mark and she had been riveted by all the details, also very concerned. Cathy had a great ability to see things from a slightly different angle, making her perspective valuable to me at my time of uncertainty. She was also a trusted friend.

The warm heavy air embraced me like a lost lover as I stepped out onto the sidewalk at the Bridgetown air-port. This was the start of the long hot Caribbean summer and judging by this day it promised to be a scorcher.

Cathy was there to pick me up and we started catching up immediately.

"Oh my gosh I'm sooo happy to see you, I can't wait to hear all your news and I've got a few things lined up for us to do while you're here!"

"Cathy, this little visit is coming at just the right time for me. I think everything over the last few months is unravelling."

By the time we finished with a quick session of catch-up we had arrived at the Divi Beach property in St. Lawrence Gap.

"Here we are," she said. "I wish I had room for you to stay at my place but wait 'till you see how small it is. A fraction of the size of my last big old place."

"No problem at all. Divi is very convenient for me, I'll be fine."

It was another time share exchange for me and the location was not only close to Cathy's house but right on a great beach with fabulously large and graceful Casuarina trees for magnificent shade. The unit itself was reasonably well appointed with all the necessary items including a small shop on the property for the extras, plus it had a pool. I was looking forward to the itinerary Cathy had mapped out for us and, after putting my things away and a quick change of clothes, we headed off to St. Philip Parish so I could see Cathy's new bungalow. It was cozy, colorful, and comfortable. Very West Indian in flavor and a better size for her than her previous large four bedroom place close to the sea.

"I have taken the liberty of pulling some things off the internet for you and you simply must read them all. You will absolutely not believe how sinister these guys can be and how dangerous and, well, I was totally blown away with how complex their operation is." Cathy seemed visibly concerned.

Cathy had just presented me with some very critical evidence supporting much, if not all, of what I had been through with Mark Smith. Things I simply couldn't see, or perhaps refused to see, while I was in the midst of it.

"You can read it on the beach but you have to read it. Promise me." She thrust a bundle of freshly printed pages of everything from internet dating sites, romance scams, fraud hotlines, victims advocacy groups, case studies, as well as how to report a con artist. The information had all been available online somewhere. I never researched any of that. I had entered into the online process with a positive and trusting attitude.

"You realize, don't you Cathy, I'm only here for a week. This is a helluva lot of reading to cover in that time!" With just a quick shuffle through the pile, I was quite appalled at the number of scammers and the extent they would go to get what they were after — and it's never love.

"I'm going to have to hope those beach lounges are comfortable and that there's a bar close by. Looks like I'll be spending a chunk of time there. Really though, Cathy, I really appreciate all the time and effort you put into preparing this homework assignment for me. I do. You're a good friend."

"No worries, Gay, I only wish I'd been able to get this organized a bit earlier, I might have been able to help you more."

"I don't think it would have made any difference. I was headstrong and really into this guy." Cathy looked sad.

"I really believed him," I continued, "I wanted to believe him so badly that I just overlooked the signs. All the signs."

"No point in beating yourself up over it now," Cathy said, then added cautiously, "I'm just glad you're coming to your senses now and realizing this guy isn't for real. You do know that NOW don't you?"

"I know it now. I do, but I still have a hard time accepting the fact that the Mark Smith I was talking to on the phone, and chatting with on the internet is not the same Mark Smith that was in the photo. I want to know who he really is."

" . . . or who SHE is" Cathy interrupted. "Wait until you read the stuff I printed off for you. You'll be amazed. These scammers can be anyone, male or female. How sickening is that!"

I was jolted by that. I had not imagined there might be some deranged woman involved in this scam but it was a possibility.

Together we spent some time scanning the various pages, reading aloud articles of particular interest, testimonials given by victims of romance scams. It was tragic really. Women had divested themselves of life savings, committed suicide, or ultimately died from a disorder that could have been cured had the money for the treatment not been diverted to a con artist.

"I think I've seen enough of this for one day. Let's think about grabbing a bite to eat."

I was tired from the trip, tired of all of this, and hungry.

"I know just the spot by the water. A friend of mine just opened this place and you'll love it."

Cathy knew everyone on the island and was sure her friend would have a wonderful place to eat. It was hard to find a bad restaurant in Barbados. At this point, anything would taste good, but I had my mind set on the pepperpot, a strong and savory stew-like dish, a combination of every this and that, and very popular there.

We were having our coffee after dinner.

"I know all this stuff about Mark has been difficult," Cathy started in, "but not to change the subject, tell me when did you last talk to Vicente?"

"Wow, that's a huge leap and it sure is a change of subject! It's been a while. Too long. Why do you ask?"

"I was just wondering. I haven't heard you mention anything about him in a while, so I didn't know if you were still in communication with him or not."

Cathy had met Vicente back when we were living together on the island and she had been very fond of him, as well as disappointed that we had parted ways years later.

"I honestly can't tell when the last time was that I spoke to him, but it's  been ages now, I bet it's been a year. He was with a woman last I heard, so I presume they are still together. He stopped calling me and although I've thought of calling him many times, I haven't had his number since he left his old job."

"Do you still miss him?" Cathy was a master of the obvious.

"I always miss him, I miss what we had together and I've struggled to get over him for years. He is one of the main reasons I agreed to pursue the online business. I was trying to get over him. I loved him so much, probably too much. Now you bring up his name again tonight."

"I was just curious," she said. "We can talk about something else, like making sure you get all the information you need to work on getting rid of this Dr. Mark Smith."

"Cathy, I would love to figure out a way to catch this guy."

"Oh, my God, don't even go there. When you finish reading all the stuff I prepared for you, you'll know how dangerous and impossible that is."

"I'll take your word for that. Thanks for the lift. Tomorrow is another day. Dinner has been great, it's always good to be back. I'm happy to see you and I need to get some sleep so I can start fresh in the morning. I'll give you a buzz when I get up and am ready to move about."

It had been a long day. We had enjoyed a full dinner and the pepperpot did not disappoint. We shared some good girl talk. I loved being back in the Caribbean again, and out of the blue Cathy had brought up Vicente's name, who was now foremost on my mind one more time.

# Under the Casuarina

*T*he sea felt wonderfully cool on such a hot sultry day. I had picked up a Bajan Kiss at the bar. (A *drink* from the bartender, not a kiss. Although the thought had fleetingly crossed my mind). This one had white rum, vanilla, and grenadine syrup nicely blended in a tall plastic glass. No umbrella. I ground the glass into the sand beside my lounger and, having slathered 100 spf sunscreen all over me, I settled back under the canopy of shade. The soft island tunes from the radio at the bar helped drown out some voices further down the beach. I picked up the stack of papers Cathy had given me and began to read.

Elizabeth Bernstein had written an article in the *Wall Street Journal* which Cathy had kindly saved for me. In it were some tips on how to protect yourself from online dating scams such as: *Pay attention to language.* Is it standard, recognizable English, or flowery phrasing that seems unfamiliar? *Use search engines.* Check for the person on social networking sites. You can add parts of his profile on a dating site, or email message, on Google or Bing or add one of the sob stories that you have been given and see if it is common. *Check out the person's photo.* You can upload a picture from the profile on theeye.com and see where on the internet that photo has appeared. *Stick to paid online dating sites.* Paid sites have a paper trail of the members through credit card information. *Download security software onto your smartphone and tablet.* Evidently there are increased attacks against routers. *Ask for more information before sharing your email or phone number.* Where does the person live and work? Make sure other sources (such as Facebook or other social sites) have the information that matches what you were given. *Get on the phone as fast as possible.* You can probably tell in a very short minute if someone is for real. *Never give money to a stranger that you have not met.* Period.

I read this section again with an eye on my own personal behavior and how I could have done things much differently. If only I had read about these things *before* I'd gotten on the dating site. I assumed I was smarter than they were, or smart enough to know how to handle myself. The article went on to discuss what psychologists refer to as the "halo effect," which happens when we notice something we like about a person. Often it is their physical appearance, and from there we imagine other positive qualities. We see an attractive person, we read an interesting profile and soon we "create" the person we are looking for, and we let our guard down, ignoring all the red flags. Online scammers love the halo effect.

"Oh my God, this is *exactly* what I've done with Mark Smith!"

The words spilled out of me in whispered but anguished tones. It's true. All of it was true. Mark had indeed talked me into getting off that site quickly, so we could chat. There is no tracing the chat lines. He did get my phone number early on, and I did detect the slight accent which I attributed to the Bahamas, I found it fascinating and I was right in the midst of the "halo effect." The language was often flowery and I hadn't really paid that much attention to the poetry aspect but I certainly had fallen into the lap of one very clever fellow.

Cathy had pulled down one single sheet of paper which was included in my reading packet. It was a personal account submitted to one of the agencies working to end online romance scams. This submission was made by wildturkey and it referenced a scammer that she had fallen for. One marksmith044@contractor.net In her brief account she said "it had taken him three weeks to scam her and that she had totally fallen for the charms of Mark R. Smith." No doubt it was also my Mark R. Smith. The name was the same, the three week period was the same, only the contractor turned veterinarian was different. A simple change in the script would have been easy.

What I had found to be the most difficult aspect of the romance scam to deal with was the fact that the photo I had come to associate with Mark R. Smith, that handsome, strong square-shaped, smiling Anglo Saxon face, was a photo of another innocent victim. Just like myself. A face that was likely stolen from a social networking page and used in a profile designed to attract someone like me. In reality, the real Mark Smith may easily have been some smarmy Nigerian or Malaysian, an unattractive man or woman who simply hijacked a photo and a profile for the scam. The thought of a group of individuals who all sat around a cyber cafe somewhere in a foreign country using a well rehearsed script to plan the scam was ugly and difficult to grasp. These scammers were adept at psychological profiling and would use any weakness they found to their advantage. They use many tricks to lure in their victims: poetry, gifts, their undying love, all to get their victims under their spell until it was the time to fabricate some "financial difficulty."

I knew none of the details of this before signing up on an online dating site. I should have been better educated to the pitfalls of this cyber dating but I was not. I am an honest person. Scamming anyone would be the furthest thing from my mind, therefore I was naive in not believing anyone would do something like this to me. Had I ever known about romancescam.com or scamdigger.com I would gladly have done some reading in advance. I would have learned that the target age is between fifty to seventy, an age group that would appear to scammers to be financially sound and romantically desperate. The user names would all look like "4real" or "4luv" and many of the first names would appear to be normal but would all end with an 's': Williams, Kevins, etc. and the last names are usually very common: Smith would be a good choice! The sentences are all slightly off for the English speaking person. For example they could say: "am Williams by name" instead of the more flowing and usual "I am William." Other phrases are mixed up, as are nouns, pronouns, singular and plural, and verb tense. The overall use of grammar as English speaking people would speak is all wrong. Often during a chat there would be long pauses. This particular feature drove me crazy but I learned that they were researching answers on the internet while I was waiting patiently at the other end for the answer. The love poems? Sadly, not original and nearly all pulled from the internet from many popular sites dealing with romance. The script they would work from would all be contrived to be tragic enough to appeal to the victim to send money. Usually Western Union was the preferred method. Once it left your hands by Western Union it would be irreversible and untraceable. The collection of people needed to pull off these scams could be staggering. Many people along the route could be pulled in to pose as the hotelier, driver, Western Union employee. Whatever actor was needed for the play, the role could be filled by someone, in exchange for a small piece of the action.

The more I read the worse it got. Mobile phones were changed out all the time if the scammer believed his calls were being traced. The cases were as numerous as the pages, and the reports of the victims were horrific. They ranged from being involved in borrowing money from others to pay the scammer, and often medical disasters would occur and life savings, treatment or surgeries forfeited by the victim because money for those treatments had been turned over to the scammer. People had gone to jail for money laundering for a scammer without realizing what they had done.

Still others had committed suicide out of sheer desperation once they discovered what had happened. What the scammer tells the victim overrides everything else in the victim's life, because the victim has been drawn so deeply into the web of deception.

I put the pages down. Picking up my second Bajan Kiss and sipping it slowly, I began to mentally review the events with Mark and the others from those first days back in February when I first signed on to the 'romance' site.

It was making sense now. All those early guys — the ones who were overseas in Malaysia — and then Mark leaving for Malaysia some weeks later . . . could it have been coincidental? I remember contacting the site to inquire about Mark Smith early on.

"I'm trying to review a few items in the profile of Mark R. Smith, could you help me find that profile?"

My reason had been quite pure at the time. I wanted more information from his profile, but he had taken it down.

"I'm sorry, but we have no Mark R. Smith registered with us on our site."

"There must be some mistake." I couldn't believe my ears. "It is Mark Smith maybe with an R for a middle initial, maybe without it but I'm positive of the name. He was listed as being from New York City."

"I'm sorry Ma'am, we do not have Mark Smith on our site. We have never had anyone by that name listed on our site. I'm sorry."

How could that have been possible? The only explanation my non-technological mind came up with was that I had been cleverly phished off the site I thought I was on. Perhaps he, or they, grabbed me and/ or my email identifying address when they saw it. They may have also grabbed other victims at the same time and weeded us out in some order. Whichever fellow I seemed to gravitate toward would become the dominant player. For a piece of the action the others would fade to the background to allow the stronger candidate to perform his scam. Mark Smith had been the one I'd gravitated toward. The rest became history. Nothing else made sense. I felt sick to my stomach.

I remember having a thought months ago about an amusing scenario where that whole first group of characters would be returning from Malaysia at the same time, experience a flight delay, find themselves rambling around the departure lounge in Kuala Lumpur and start a conversation with each other. They would learn they were all returning to the states to meet the new love interest, pass around a photo which would be a downloaded photo of me from the dating site! When I initially had this thought, I was openly amused by it. It was no longer amusing at all.

The laugh was clearly on me. Dammit!

All the names and titles, head of Agra-Industry for Malaysia — all fake. Airline documents for a flight on Emirates air through Dubai into Kuala Lumpur all fake, and of course also the original million dollar contract, all fake.

The land lines were probably located in hotel rooms, back rooms, or boiler rooms; something temporary. Cell phones would be anonymous and untraceable. These guys could be operating from any foreign country in the world as well as right in the United States. Phone calls can be transferred to any number anywhere by any phone anywhere. Who knew?

Later I would learn that about five of these guys identifying email addresses were located in one center in Sunnyvale California registered to an "executive suite" of an unnamed business.

I learned that the con artist will determine your personality profile and identify your needs. Maybe focus on your pride or ego, your dreams and your visions of riches or your religious convictions. Whatever would work best for the situation. What a complete jerk I had been. How, I asked myself, could Mark Smith determine what my needs were long before I had even figured that out for myself?

I can now think of many different questions I could have asked that might have led me to an earlier recognition of who I had been dealing with. His business or veterinarian license number would have been a good start.

I had tried, earlier on, to track down both his veterinary degree and his license number but I was not able to get any information on either search.

Was he affiliated with the Chamber of Commerce in Texas? I was unable to gain access to the University of London alumnae group without a proper password. I was not an alumna, so that was a dead end. I also tried for any information at all from the roster for the American Veterinary Association. Something, anything, but nothing! Whatever I did clearly wasn't enough, and when others had done research and came up with nothing, I accepted that as a sign that there was nothing to find, therefore there was no problem. Instead of realizing that for a veterinarian who travels internationally, for such extraordinary sums on contracts, to never have published one paper under his name was impossible. I simply dismissed it all, believing that whenever we had a chance to meet we could sort it all out. Really? How could I have ignored *all* the signs?

Why had Mark targeted me, I wondered? Many con artists are educated, well read individuals who probably show psychopathic tendencies. To many it is simply a game, a game that provides an enormous adrenaline rush. Mark Smith was a psychological illusionist, able to convince me, or anyone, to believe in the illusion he fabricated. I did. When I believed him, my dignity and self respect left me.

So many times over the past month I had wanted to cry, to be able to release all the tension, hurt, and anger that had been building throughout this situation. I was torn between wanting to cry at the deception and the emotional rape, and mourning the loss of a love. A love that was never really there. Seductive words coming from a script, delivered by a computer stashed away in a dark boiler room probably somewhere in Nigeria or Malaysia. Nauseating.

I closed my eyes and saw the face that, to me, had been Mark Smith. The handsome guy in the white starched shirt. I instantly felt sad for myself knowing that he was not real, but I also felt sad for that handsome man. Who had *he* been? Someone's lover, father, relative or friend; his face had likely been stolen from a social networking site and he, like me, had been an unknowing victim of this scam.

# *Interlude*

$\mathcal{I}$t had been a troublesome day of reflection. It would take some time to become fully detached from all the unreal photos and phone calls and other events that had occupied my last four months. In the past when I had the need to work through things I had always found answers at the water's edge.

My need to go to Barbados had been no accident. Cathy had provided a wealth of information which had helped me get a handle on what had happened and how, and the comfort of knowing I had not been the only woman ever taken in by a clever scammer. I also had found a supportive ear and sounding board in Cathy. Together we spent many hours running through scenarios looking for puzzle pieces. Even though those pieces came in a variety of shapes, they fit together to complete the picture.

I drank down the last of my Bajan Kiss and slipped into my sandals, stuffed the papers into my beach bag, and tossed the empty plastic glass into the trash bin. From the radio came a song that had a distinctive reggae rhythm but it was the lyrics that made me smile: "Give Me Everything Tonight 'Cause We May Not Get Tomorrow." I had to smile at the thought of how West Indian that notion was. I shuffled on down the path toward my room, still smiling, and thinking about Vicente and wondering what he might be doing all these many years later.

I had forced my mind to avoid lingering on him for quite some time but, with being in the Caribbean, those sweet memories were all returning. I missed him dreadfully but we were not together and I had no choice but to push the thought of him to the back of my mind again and try to forget. He had been the love of my life. We had lived together, shared a pleasant life, then ended our relationship. I tried to get over him and thought if I left the Caribbean it might be easier. I moved to Florida. End of story.

I knew that part of how I got into this online mess was my need to find something, or someone, to help me get Vicente out of my mind. I was on the right track, but I'd gotten horribly derailed online. Back in Barbados now reminded me of the last time Vicente and I had come to visit Cathy.

"It's a beautiful day, Sweetie, what do you say we try the pool, then hang out at the beach?"

Vicente loved hanging out on the beach, particularly in Barbados. He loved the people watching, the abundance of shade, and the usual presence of a little tiki bar. His needs were simple.

"Cathy is going to swing by a bit later and join us, so we need another lounge chair and the large umbrella, and keep the girl watching to a minimum, please!" I loved to tease him but I knew he enjoyed that sport as much as any other. He was a very handsome man and women were attracted to him.

"You know I only have eyes for you, Sweetie." He smilingly scampered over the hot sand to the tiki bar for a few drinks with tiny umbrellas. That had been a lovely day, the sea was warm, there was a delightful breeze, we enjoyed ourselves and all seemed right with the world. I didn't know then that it would be our last trip to this island together.

I had a ton of work to review, thanks to Cathy's research, and dwelling on what was or might have been was only going to be sad and unproductive. I grabbed a stack of the papers and began working my way through them. All thoughts of Vicente would have to be savored later.

Dinner with Cathy was always another culinary experience. She had so many connections on island that it was always wonderful to meet the newest or best known chef and sample the cuisine. Restaurants in Barbados were all superb and it was difficult to choose the best. Most had dramatic sea views, often suspended from a high cliff, while a crashing surf could be seen just below.

I recounted to her the various snippets of information I had been able to review that day. All things I wished I had learned many months earlier. I had not. Everything was for a reason, and while I am not sure why I had been targeted on those sites, or so gullible, I am sure that everything that I had experienced online had happened to me for some reason. Whatever that was.

I went back to my condo, slipped into my nightgown

and lay there for what seemed to be hours. My thoughts were of Vicente again and what he was doing and with whom. Damn! I wish I could keep him out of my mind. It hurt my heart to think of him. I switched to wondering about the online events, Mark Smith, and all the cast of characters. Somehow I needed to turn this into a positive experience, for me and perhaps for others. I would sleep on it and let other thoughts go for now.

I awoke early with a plan formulating in my mind. I would get this experience all down on paper, and share it with others. I would write about it. For now, I would shower and get ready to have breakfast with Cathy. We had a lovely boat tour planned for the day.

"Cathy, I came up with a plan last night and I'm curious about your opinion."

"Let's hear it." She did not look the least bit curious but later admitted she thought I was creating a plan for dinner.

"This online dating meeting experience has been unnerving for me but think of the hundreds of people out there who get caught up in similar situations like this every day, or even worse."

"I know," Cathy replied, "and after reading those papers and various scenarios that I found for you it's really criminal that so many scammers are out there. Where did they all come from?"

"I don't know, but I know they've found some way to be successful at what they do so there will be hundreds more out there as time goes on. Millions maybe, and that's what I wanted to talk to you about."

"Oooh, okay, now I want to hear what this is about."

We had a scheduled boat trip planned for today. A sightseeing tour that would take us up one side of the coast and back. I loved being on the water and I was really looking forward to this day.

The catamaran was now swinging around the southern coast and preparing to drop anchor so we could snorkel among the small brown sea turtles in the area. We could continue our talk in the water.

"I think I need to write about my experience with this process. Who knows, but maybe if one other person would take the time to research things, or even read about *my* experiences, it would all be worth it."

"I think it's a marvelous idea and you certainly have enough information to share. Go for it!"

The turtles were amazingly friendly and curious creatures. Their shelled bodies made them look awkward yet they were totally graceful swimming in their habitat. Our time in the water seemed far too short, the turtles were swimming so close to us but since feeding them was against the law they were close out of curiosity and with a trusting heart. I could relate to that.

"Yes," I said when we were toweling off on the deck, "I think that's exactly what I'll do, I will try to write about this."

The catamaran was approaching the western coast, home of the deservedly famous Sandy Lane resort. We had snorkeled over coral reefs, been swimming with the brown sea turtles and sampled a tasty barbecue and some Myers rum punch concoctions and were happily sailing back to Bridgetown. We talked a lot about my plan, about the dating information, and Vicente.

On the way to the hotel we stopped into the Waterfront Cafe to speak with a few of Cathy's friends before heading off to dinner. Tapas was the restaurant we chose, another fine dining experience right on the water. We had enjoyed a superb day and ended it with an extraordinary meal, as well as our wet sandy toes!

The following day Cathy had arranged a tour for me to see monkeys, cane fields, old parish churches, more magnificent beaches, huge boulders at Bathsheba on the rugged Atlantic coast, and quaint pastel colored chattel houses, fine boutiques and small shopping areas. I stopped for a bite of lunch at the Pottery Works and browsed for a few brightly colored pieces to add to my small collection, plus a few hand painted works of art. The crab and Banks beer slid down nicely in the heat of the afternoon, and soon I was back at the hotel in time to change, and meet Cathy. Fine dining in Barbados was not only an art form but also a pastime.

I had been there one week. I had spent every day with Cathy, mostly talking about my thoughts on the papers she researched for me. We had eaten marvelous food, been on some very interesting tours and I had read enough literature on the various romance scams to go back home and take a long hard look at the site and make a decision on what to do about going forward.

Coming to Barbados had been a very good experience for me. A perfect interlude from the stress of the previous months. I had loved spending time with Cathy. She had been exactly the kind of friend I had needed then, informative and supportive. Barbados was wonderful. My mind was on Vicente, and it had nothing to do with the Caribbean. I simply missed him, still.

# Back in the Saddle

Delsey was also disappointed and discouraged with my online attempts to date.

"I'm really sorry this didn't work out for you, Gay." She had been apologetic.

"It's certainly not *your* fault it didn't work out. I know you were trying to help but the circumstances were beyond anyone's comprehension, particularly mine!"

"Well, at least it's not a total waste of time. You will write about it and maybe save others from falling into the same situation. Still, I feel bad."

"I know you do, but please don't. It was a huge experience for me regardless of how it's turned out. Who knows, maybe someone will still turn out to be Prince Charming."

I suppose it could be argued that my time had been wasted in part, because no one was real. Oh, a few were real, but they were so far off the mark of what I was looking for that it was ridiculous. Mark Smith had begun as a fun, albeit unbelievable romance but had quickly fizzled into a complicated and dubious experience of a totally different nature.

Sam had experienced strange fellows as well, and when I connected with him he had an announcement of his own.

"I have about decided to remove myself from the process and not bother with the site any longer. Issues at work are taking up most of my time and I find it all to be too difficult and unrewarding a situation to continue. Therefore I'm dismantling my profile and moving on with my life."

Hard to argue with that logic.

"I think I probably have two viable choices," I said. "One choice would be to shut down my profile as well. I could wrap it up and call it a day. Except that it would seem pointless after having spent so many months online and with no success."

"You're right, that's about the way I see it for both of us." Sam had agreed.

"Sam, I've passed through so much crap already and yet I haven't accomplished what I set out to do and that was to find a good man."

"Okay, so what's your other option?" Sam had that oh-no-not-again look on his face.

"My other choice would be to simply get back into the saddle and find another rodeo."

"You would really put yourself through that again?" he asked.

"I would certainly be better armed with knowledge this time around, don't you think?"

"That's a given. I think we've both learned a lot."

"Besides, it would give me another shot at gathering up more information for my book."

"In a masochistic sort of way, I s'pose your right."
Sam didn't seem totally convinced but was trying his
best to be supportive.

Delsey had joined Cathy in her support of my
writing venture, as had others, but they were all nervous
about my being online.

I spent some time entering my profile and posting a
photo on another site. The process was getting old
but I had a new sense of motivation driving me for
time number three. (Third time's the charm?) This site
guaranteed finding a mate to make you 'sizzle.'

*Considering what the previous cast of characters*
*provided, certainly nothing short of a three alarm fire,*
*could provide any kind of sizzle.* However, in good
faith, I posted my completed profile, took a deep breath
and waited.

The first group of fellows to float into my life on the
new site certainly did not add the promised 'sizzle.' In
the interest of fairness, however, I did read each
profile carefully and narrowed them down to four
with whom I believed some communication would
even be possible or remotely acceptable. All four had
approached me first, politely asking if they could
contact me, usually by email, and since the site itself
provided the mechanism to do that without exchanging
personal email addresses, it seemed a harmless enough
gesture.

Harold was early sixties and lived in Ohio — a bit

further than the fifty mile radius policy of the previous site. He seemed straightforward enough but after only two emails I determined he was not exciting enough to engage my interest.
Delete.

Kelvin did live within the fifty mile radius but with a fifteen year old son. That thought was beyond scary. (Raising teen aged boys can help remind you why wolves will eat their young!) Taking on someone else's teenager was not an option for me.
Delete.

Chris lived just within the fringe of the fifty mile zone, but during an initial chat something sounded too familiar about his employment of buying and selling jewels and gemstones; and visions of another man, on another site came to mind. I asked him one too many questions which he chose to ignore and I got tired of asking.
Delete.

Rick was an odd fellow from the start and I chose to not spend any time trying to figure him out. Not worth pursuing.
Delete.

So that took care of week number one and the arrival of the first wave. It was much as I had expected, but it was only the first week.
The second week became far more interesting.

After many months of not hearing from him, Mark Smith sent an email. I had not communicated with him at all. I was stunned.

"It pains me not to be near you my darling, for you are always in my thoughts as I hope I am still in yours."

He had left a few text messages and phone messages but when I had ignored them he had resorted back to the email.

"I don't know what you mean when you ask what the next obstacles will be to keep me over here. You know my every intention is to leave here as fast as possible and come straight to you. You are still going to meet me at the airport aren't you?"

*Oh sure, I'd love to meet you at the airport in a long black limousine, a big brass band, and a firing squad if I could!*

"You will think of something to keep you in Malaysia I'm sure." That had been my only response.

It had almost seemed to be a ridiculous question under the circumstances. How indeed could he assume I would still be going to pick him up at the airport? He knew I had not communicated with him for months. What was he thinking? My other question was what in the world would Mark R. Smith do to plan his endgame? Maybe this was it. Was he setting the stage for the grand finale? That was still to be determined. At one point during a later communication, I was convinced that he was trying to bait me into an argument. Maybe it was my imagination, and though I could not remember his exact words, I felt that he was definitely steering me in that direction. I had read that this behavior was not to be unexpected. The argument would deteriorate into a shouting match, blow up, and the relationship would be over. Simple. I'll never know, as I disengaged myself from the communication. How does a con artist end something? *Do they ever truly end something, or forever drag things out?*

I read of cases where, when the stakes were very high, it could become a kidnapping or even a murder. For a petty ante romance scam it was usually just a fight, or a simple drop of contact. That didn't seem quite fair to me, considering how many months I had been involved with this. It also didn't seem to be very like something Mark would do. *What the hell was fair about Dr. Mark R. Smith?*

My curiosity was going to win the day. I wanted to know how it would end. I would wait this out. The damage had already been done. I had already given up the money and learned what that had accomplished. I had figured out who and what he really was not. I was no longer able to be hurt by him. I had taken every precaution to protect myself against any kind of identify theft through locked down access to all personal information. I would damn well learn what he had in mind to end this. I would become the actor he had become. I would let him write the script, I would act my part, and I would wait.

# The Second Wave

*C*alvin was a fifty-seven year old living in Colorado.

"I apologize for my accent in advance," he had emailed me, "but I am interested to contact you by phone."

"Give me *your* number and I will call *you*." I thought that was a better plan. When I finally got through to the number he had given me, his accent was indeed difficult and the cell phone turned out to be a land line which was a magic jack phone registered any-where. Calvin was deleted. This was getting easier.

Alex seemed to be an interesting man. He was an engineer who was apparently working in Istanbul at the time of the contact.

"I am renting a small apartment for a few weeks in Istanbul while I finish up a big construction project." *I could see myself holding up a large red flag and waving it.*

"Why don't you use the landline in the apart-ment?" I had thought that was a simple question.

"Because there is no land line inside this apart-ment."

*Who the hell would rent an apartment to a busi-*

*ness person anywhere today without phone lines and cable inside?* His next sentence was the kicker.

"I use my cell phone for work and to keep in touch with the guys in the field. Like last night, there was a bad accident and one of the workers had a big truck roll over on him and squash his legs so he had to be rushed to surgery."

"That's terrible." *Now why don't you get to the point of all of this?*

"The doctor wanted me to post seven thousand dollars toward the surgery."

*There it is — that's the point* and he continued with the permission the doctor had given Alex to ask people to donate money toward his recovery! I told him I didn't believe a word of his story.

"If you don't trust me then perhaps we shouldn't communicate any further."

He was absolutely right on that point. Alex joined the list of the deleted.

Carlos was a handsome Italian who had moved to Kentucky from Rome. His wife had died and he now did a little traveling to Italy annually to buy precious stones. (There's the ever popular precious stone purveyor but in a tiny area of Kentucky?) That seemed totally implausible from the beginning. The second day he sent a poem to brighten my day. It may have done that, under different circumstances, but in this instance I had seen that poem before. Mark Smith had sent it to me months ago. Carlos' story and poem just bombed and he too was deleted.

John was fascinating. His photo profile looked like he was a male model. The two other photos he included with the profile he must have thought also looked like him, but I did not. John claimed to be a telecommunication engineer in San Francisco. In our first chat I asked, "You mentioned you were a telecommunication engineer, tell me about that, what exactly do you do?"

"I work on rigging things on poles, those large structures that run and hold cable lines, things like that."

*No, I don't know about things like that, my cable lines are all underground!*

"No, no I don't really understand but why don't you tell me about the scope of work for an aerospace historian."

"Well, I, uh, it's complicated. Why do you want to know that?"

"Because, your profile states that is a passion of yours. It sounds interesting so I thought you could tell me about it."

Instead, John continued to explain about his telecommunication work. He didn't recognize his own reconstructed profile, and clearly was a scammer. John was deleted.

*Later, upon figuring out it was undoubtedly I who had turned him into the dating site, he sent me an email. In it, as further testimony to his character, he told me I should go fuck myself. An offer I chose to decline.*

Patrick was an Irishman living in Santa Barbara, CA whose profile indicated he was in the music business in the Los Angeles area. When I inquired about the nature of the music business I was told it was really his friend who was in the music business; Patrick had just moved to California from Dublin.

"Do you know where County Cork is?" I had set that question up immediately.

"No," came his response. He then went on to explain that after he arrived in Los Angeles he had sold his house "and I moved *down* there."

"The fact is, Patrick, you would have moved *up* there from LA to Santa Barbara." Patrick was deleted.

*No explanation of how you can be from Dublin and not have heard of County Cork!*

I was getting faster and better at recognizing these inconsistencies. A bit late, I admit, but still I was improving. I was also reporting all of these people to the dating site for being scammers and/or fraudsters. Amazingly enough, I received a polite email from the site in response:

"We thank you for being forthcoming and reporting these individuals to us. We apologize for the fact that while we take every precaution to carefully screen perspective users of our site, it is an overwhelming task to screen each person thoroughly. We rely on people like you to bring things to our attention and help us maintain the integrity of the site."

I did not see it exactly the same way. There had been such an enormous number of them that I was quite appalled. I had not gone looking for any of these people, nor had I originally contacted any of them. They had contacted *me*, and I had responded with trepidation and with as acute an eye as possible, to what they wrote. I was, in my view, doing the job that somebody on the staff of this site should have been doing.

Once they were reported I did notice that these scammers all disappeared from the site within a day or two at the most. I felt somewhat satisfied that at least they would not be around to harm me, or others.

That was inaccurate. Within about three days after seeing them removed, I decided to explore the site to make sure these scammers were all gone. To my surprise three of them were back on the site! They used the same photos. Some wore slightly different shirts in the photos, or had a secondary photo which had been substituted for the original one. New numbers had been assigned to these men and in a few cases the birth dates and zodiac signs had changed. The men were identical. I fired off a second email to the site:

"How can it be that people who are reported to you on Monday, are taken off the site Tuesday, and put back up on the site on Wednesday? This seems to be undisciplined and you should be doing a better job of policing your site to protect the *paying* public from this sort of evil. Certainly the public has a right to protection. You are not doing nearly enough. You have been given all their original member numbers, I have also provided all the newly assigned numbers and it is apparent there is NO online security despite your claims to the contrary."

The response I received was amusing.

"We thank you again for your active participation

in making our dating site more enjoyable for all its users."

*I guess they're referring to all the scammer users, because my interests are not protected.*

"We appreciate your assistance with eliminating these people from our site. To show our appreciation we will offer to credit you with three more months on this site."

*Really! That's it? Three whole more months of the same exhausting and dangerous crap? I will be happy to fire you off another email and tell you where you can shove each one of these guys, your three free shitty months, and your dating site! No deal.*

Larry contacted me in a somewhat different manner. I was researching the site to see if any of the second rounders had managed to find themselves back online again when Larry interrupted on the instant messenger screen to ask if I could chat with him immediately. He seemed too eager to chat, only to tell me he was leaving for Chicago in the morning for a few days of business.

*So why try to fit in this 'get acquainted' chat before you go? I'm not that interested in you anyway.* He was abrasive in tone but that paled in comparison to his next big question.

"If you are divorced how do you pay for your mortgage?"

"I fail to see how that is any of your concern. I am an adult. I own my own home and the rest is not your concern."

"I'll offer to send you some money so you can pay

your mortgage. I have a large sum of money, coming from a huge contract I had with a previous business deal with the Nigerian National Petroleum Commission. Let me send you a gift to help take care of you."

*Any time I hear that a man wants to take care of me it has to be a 'first,' and in this case also a 'last.'*

I heard the word Nigeria in there and decided my 'gift' was really Larry's way of having me launder his money from this business deal. Larry was quickly deleted.

It was overwhelming and amazing how there could possibly be so very many con artists around, all earning a living from romance scams. It was staggering. How many people had been fooled by these guys? Not always guys. Women were also scamming men. Men were scamming men. Women were also posing as men and scamming women. The dregs of the human species. Certainly I had not been lucky, but others I had spoken to about their experiences shared stories of themselves that were nothing like mine.

How was this happening? The only thing I had done wrong so far was to go on these sites at all. I had tried to be cautious. I had asked numerous questions. I had tried to verify all the information these men had supplied me. I was skeptical about the lack of questions asked of me, and of languages, accents, phone lines, and even the type set and script on computers being used for emails and chats. Was it different from previous communication? What time of day were these emails arriving? If it was between one and around five in the morning there was a good chance it was arriving from some overseas destination: Nigeria, Malaysia, anywhere in Europe. I had even tracked down four of these scammers to a corporate account listed only as that, in Sunnyvale California.

I had tried my best to be diligent. It had not worked.

I was very discouraged, I had not achieved what I had set out to do and I had certainly put myself through much trouble, not to mention hard work, hours of research, and a long ride on an emotional roller coaster that had no brakes.

# The Real (Deal?)

*N*othing can remain the same forever. Sooner, or later, a change must come.

His name was Oscar. He had a strong handsome young face with white hair, which he kept in a teddy bear cut, and dark black eyes framed with thick dark eyebrows. He found me one morning while I was checking my email and he had sent me a message.

"I am intrigued by your photo and would like to contact you."

I was intrigued myself and felt that it certainly was about time for someone new to appear in my life. Someone real. I was deserving of that, and eager. I hoped that this one would be real, but I could only hope.

Oscar seemed a bit laid back, maybe more reserved; respectful and cautious from the beginning. That seemed a refreshing change from the others. Unlike the others, he had not mentioned the love word in the first sentence or the first week, nor did he use intimate terms of endearment in the initial contact. I thought this was an excellent beginning.

I was interested in his profile. He lived and worked in an affluent suburb of Atlanta, had studied engineering and surveying in Madrid and had been educated there as a young boy and had completed college before returning to the Atlanta area.

"My parents divorced during my childhood and I was sent to live with my mother who was Spanish and working in Spain at the time."

The foreign aspect of his experiences was of interest to me, more so than was the average guy living down the road. That average meat and potatoes guy was never one to catch my attention. I loved the foreign flavor.

"I was educated in Madrid, at the University" he continued, "and got a job later with a big surveying and engineering company over there and finally came back to the states and settled in Atlanta, where I work now."

Europeans were generally well traveled, at least within Europe, as opposed to Americans, many of whom had never traveled beyond the boundary of their own state. Maybe it is because of my own exposure to foreign countries and cultures but I gravitate to those who have had shared experiences.

"I love to cook, play golf in my free time and I absolutely love to dance."

Oscar had just scored major points with that trinity of activities.

I had developed an interest in Latin music with its sexy rhythms and sultry lyrics. I have always found it to be terribly romantic, and I could visualize myself doing a lively Salsa with Oscar in some cozy corner of a dance floor somewhere. I suspected he was light on his feet and he had mentioned more than once how much he loved to dance. That was beyond appealing to me. Hugging, set to music. I don't know who invented the idea but it was a fantastic one.

We soon became comfortable with the instant messaging chats and tried to chat at least twice a day as his schedule allowed. He worked from his home and had an office in town. I was trying very hard to keep the brakes on and not get too taken with this man, but I did find him interesting.

"I've been divorced for about twelve years," he told me, "and have three grown kids, but none of them live at home." *That arrangement works for me.*

"I've been on this site for a while," he then added "I'm trying hard to make sure I don't get hurt again in any relationship."

I did find him interesting. I asked a slew of standard questions and he answered them forthrightly and quickly; there were no interminably long pauses where he could be accused of googling answers. I had learned a few things over these past months and one was that a long pause was a big red flag.

We spent time getting acquainted by chat messaging, and his grammar was flawless. That in itself was an improvement.

"I presume you speak Spanish, Oscar, but I never asked you that before."

His affirmative response was rapidly produced in Spanish on a Spanish keyboard, suggesting fluency and perhaps a need for Spanish in his business. That made sense and gave credence to his involvement with a big engineering and surveying firm based in Spain and Gibraltar. I had been able to verify everything he had told me to date regarding his past and present. He was listed in the white pages with a real address and had an account on Facebook with the same picture as the one in his dating site profile. How could it be that finally, *finally* someone appeared to be the real deal?

He presented himself as a man who loved to cook and dance. I couldn't tell which attribute pleased me more, so I went with both. My favorite thing to do in any kitchen, particularly mine, would be to *watch* a man cook! How I hoped all this finally could be working out. His good looks continued to play with my mind every time I logged onto the instant chat site. Another photo of him would appear as a signature photo for the instant message site, so I had a few great photos to look at each time we were in contact. I liked that face. I liked that smile, those dark shining eyes and that this was a man who seemed, thus far, to have many of the qualities I was looking for; that was encouraging.

Within a few weeks his tone during our messaging chats had warmed, yet remained totally respectful. I could tell that he was becoming more comfortable with me and that had inspired the warmer tone of his chats, and after nearly two months of constant communicating with me fairly regularly, he told me he was in love.

That could have been a deal breaker and the raising of a tiny red flag but I had learned that men process information differently from women. A man will visually investigate a woman and often not need to go much further than that. Back to the face, breasts and the whole swimsuit fantasy. A woman, however, will visually determine only whether she wishes to continue gathering more information about a man, and then will use that information to move on to explore other things she needs or wants to know about him before making the ultimate decision of whether he will be right for her or not.

I was *not* in love with Oscar, just fascinated. I always looked forward to hearing from him and noticed that when I went offline, he would go offline as well. Perhaps I was the only one with whom he had established a chatting situation; that's what he told me.

As time went by he tried to draw me closer.

"I'm really beginning to care a lot for you, but I think you figured that out. I wish I could drive over there and meet you, but I have too much work for that right now."

"What kind of things are you working on now?"

I was curious how he could remain busy all the time and rarely even get to play a round of golf.

"I'm working on a huge project for a shopping mall and it's complicated and takes up lots of my time between drawing, phone calls etc. but I do want to come see you."

"I'd like that. When do you think that might be?"

"Maybe in a few weeks. By then the mall project will be completed."

"That sounds good. Oscar, I would like to get to know more about you but it's too hard to do with the chatting process. I really hate this process. Why don't you call me later, perhaps we could make some good progress that way and I would love to hear your voice."

"I have your number, so I will call you later, around eight if that's okay."

*Oh that's better than okay you have no idea how good that will be.*

"I'll look forward to your call around eight then." I was trying to keep composed but this would be a big step in the right direction.

It was nearly ten o'clock when I took Oliver outside for his final potty, locked the door and turned out the lights. I had no idea why I didn't hear from Oscar but perhaps I would learn something in the morning. Until then I would remain unimpressed.

The following day, his email said:

"My friends call me The See, because they say I have the gift of seeing into the future." I wondered if that was the big explanation.

"Does that gift allow you to see how I felt when you didn't phone last night?"

"I was called away to my neighbor's house for an emergency," he said, "and it was very late when I got home, I didn't want to be rude."

"I was disappointed, so call me back now. I'm home." I thought it was a grand idea and a test.

"I only wanted to tell you I was sorry about last night and tell you I had a great dream about you last night and I'll be online tonight about seven."

*So that's it, a great dream and no phone call? That smells like crap to me. This road was looking all too familiar.*

"I'll see whether I will be here and have time then or not, I have a lot of things to do later."

*The last thing I intend to do is to sit around and wait for your dumb ass to try to contact me again.*

"I'll chat with you later for sure."

I felt no need, and had no interest in responding to that. I was weary waiting for a phone call which seemed simple enough to accomplish. I now was wary of anyone who was so unwilling to use a phone. He had to be hiding something.

During some subsequent chats I uncovered a few things that I didn't agree with, and certainly the fact that he still had not phoned was at the top of my list. I would ignore him for a day or two and then received a quick message online.

"I miss you, where are you?"

One of the things he had mentioned to me was that he was a practical joker and it was becoming clear that I was not certain where his joke left off and the truth began. I hoped the joke was not on me. For a virtual relationship he was becoming tedious. Too much effort involved in trying to verify everything. I was tired of it all.

I had thought I might have found the real person but still we had not met. Hell, we hadn't even spoken on the phone!

# Introspection

$\mathcal{J}$ am most comfortable when my surroundings are in order. I love having a tidy and attractive home, though ironically I personally hate *cleaning* house. I love Clorox-clean toilets and shiny kitchen counters as much as I hate dust bunnies and finger prints — but what was there about my mental housekeeping, I asked myself, that allowed characters of fraud and deception to enter my cerebral house in such abundance?

I first looked at what might be lacking in me emotionally. Was it loneliness? I didn't believe it was. I had always had many friends, good friends, and never considered myself to be a lonely person. I was genuinely interested in doing things with others and always found a friend to share experiences with. I certainly never felt that I needed to be with a man to feel validated or wothy. Certainly not. Nor had I ever felt insecure or uncomfortable in my own skin. Quite the opposite. Iwas usually the one at a party to go up to a stranger and introduce myself and draw others into a conversation. I rather liked that. It was always easy for me to see things for others; it was a lot harder to see things for myself.

Right before the death knell on my marriage rang

out, I was sitting in a counselors' office trying to get a handle on my emotional transition from marriage to divorce.

"Gay, I want you to go home and think about something this week and when you come back next week we can talk about it. Does that sound reasonable?"

"Yes, so what is it you want me to think about?"

"One question, and one question only. I want you to think about your answer."

"Okay." I was curious, "..so what's the question?"

"What are you getting out of this marriage?"

"That's it. That's the question?" It seemed far too simple.

"Yes, just think about that and I'll see you next week at the same time."

All week I pondered that question. Such a simple thing, one simple sentence, and with it the virtual elimination of a twenty-five year marriage.

Why was I having such a hard time mustering up an answer? The following week at exactly the same time I sat there explaining to this counselor that I had given this a great deal of thought. It was really hard for me and I must have been overlooking many things.

"Why do you say you overlooked something?"

"Because, all week I thought about your question but I came up with absolutely nothing."

"*That* is your answer!" It couldn't boil down to such a simple one word response. Nothing, and yet it truly was nothing. There was nothing at all in that marriage for me. It is often the simple questions you ask that bring the results you need.

I was attempting to be my own counselor now and ask myself the same simple question. I needed to know how I had become so vulnerable to so much of this negative energy swirling around online.

Among the papers that Cathy had given me while I was in Barbados, was a printout from an article that she had found online, that had never made it to the top of my pile while I was there. This was part of an article on emotions, in a paper by John Ruskan, called *Emotional Cleaning*.

In the section on relationships Ruskan said:

"We have a genuine need for relationships of all types: to be part of a community, to work with others; to be a parent; to be intimate as well as a need to be alone. Relationships are also important because others serve as mirrors, reflecting our suppressed qualities and stimulating growth.

"In our society we have developed a special compulsiveness about one specific kind of relationship with integrity from developing. We become dependent on the relationship, even when it is not living up to what we expected from it, and dependency results in stress and the likelihood of the relationship failing. Because we are not fully enlightened yet, it is probably safe to assume that most of our relationships will be of a dependent nature, in spite of our best intentions. However, there is no problem in this, if only we can accept the pain that dependency brings.

"Pain is felt whenever what you are addicted to in the relationship is threatened or absent; this is the simplest method of identifying addictions. You may respond to the pain by arguing that your needs are legitimate or that your partner is being unfair. You may rationalize your needs endlessly, but in the end, it comes down to being addicted and dependent. Moreover, you attract the kind of person who acts exactly to trigger your insecurities. Such is the precision of Karma. You will be with someone who will make you conscious of your addictions; that *is* why you chose them.

*"Use your relationship as a vehicle for growth."*

"Whenever you feel pain in any type of relationship, whether insecurity, sexual frustration, rejection, anger, hurt, invalidation, or loneliness, you must remember that you are responsible for the pain because it is caused by your suppressed energies that are surfacing. These energies surface when you are denied those qualities or behavior in your partner to which you are addicted and which enable you to continue to suppress your pain. If you can remember this and not blame the other, you make it possible to maintain the relationship. The relationship can be used to help identify what you are addicted to, and it becomes a powerful vehicle for growth. However, if you blame the other, growth does not occur, and the relationship collapses."

"Relationship addiction can tie into any level of being, such as Security, where we depend on the other for material support; Sexual, where we are compulsive and using; Power, where we control the other because we gain energy from them; or Heart, where we seek to escape from loneliness."

It was an interesting look at some things I had not thought of about myself. I would never have considered myself addicted to a relationship, although, during the past months I had indeed been obsessive about things. My anxiety to believe what I was being told, my interest in checking online frequently to see what messages there might be, could look like an addiction. The scammers were addicted as well. They depended on the relationship for their Security and material support and the Power where they would gain energy through their control and manipulation. I had to ask myself the obvious. So, if I had chosen someone who will make me conscious of my addictions, why in the hell did I need to choose quite so *many* in such a short amount of time?  Some answers I may never know, but if learning about this and giving it thought would ultimately be a vehicle for growth, then it was important to grow. I was prepared to grow like Jack's beanstalk.

# *Why*

$\mathcal{T}$he big question is always why. Why does anyone risk so much to possibly gain so little? The online meeting or dating scene is a minefield at best. Men and women can live a vicarious life virtually, with the hope of never being discovered for who they really are, or what they really want. That aspect is particularly frightening, and various episodes of how things can go horribly wrong have been the subject of several documentaries and programs on television. Naturally, though the audience could be riveted to the often sordid details of people's lives, the pervasive thought is it could never happen to them. My guess would be that likely ten years ago the online dating was far less risky and yielded far more positive results than what happens in today's world.

We all know people who have met their partners online and remain happily united to this day. I am certain the statistics for success have dramatically changed over the years. There is so much to worry about today. One could argue that it takes all the fun out of online dating when you have to constantly second guess someone's motives, or spend hours online trying to verify information about where someone works or lives, or if they are really married or widowed or divorced as they suggest. It is beyond time consuming and no matter how 'Google-able' we are as a society, there are just some things that cannot be checked or verified, at least not by the average person. The technology is available to make telephone calls appear to be coming from any targeted area. Photographs can be pulled down in bulk from any number of social network sites and when asked for another photo, they could be accessed from a collection and sent to look like you were just taking it right from a scrapbook in front of you. Profiles can be contrived or simply stolen from others who took the time to write good profiles. Photographs can be substituted. Men you may think you are speaking to could really be women. Someone from Ohio could really be in a bank of computers in a small café speaking from blocks away, or in a small closet, perhaps a basement, or in Nigeria. I would vouch for the fact that this was *not* fun.

Perhaps one of the more sinister aspects to this process was, for me, the encounter with the sociopathic personality. I had no previous experience with that, but what I did have was a strong sense that there had to be some grave imbalance within a con artist's mind that would allow him, or her, to act out these virtual relationships repeatedly and then, when necessary, seamlessly change the story-line and relationship again and again.

I went online to try to better understand, and what I learned was that people who suffer from sociopathic disorders tend to be superficially charming. They also tend to display behavior which includes manipulation of people around them, and the desire to be in control of everything and everyone around them; that usually leads to grave consequences and shallow emotions.

There is even a profile rendered by two PhD's, H.Gleckley and R.H are:

- **Glibness and Superficial Charm** — when really they are hostile and domineering. Their victims are simply instruments to be used.
- **Manipulative and Conning**
- **Grandiose Sense of Self**
- **Pathological Lying,** making it look cool and easy.
- **Lack of Remorse, Shame, or Guilt** — the end always justifies the means.
- **Shallow Emotions** — they are not moved by anything, and they're not genuine. There is an incapacity for love
- **Need for Stimulation** — mostly they can be promiscuous and gamblers
- **Lack of Empathy** — only contempt and willingness to take advantage.
- **Lack of Behavioral Controls** — outrage to abuse because they know no boundaries
- **Early Behavior Problems** — as young children they are irresponsible and can't accept blame for what they have committed. Often have police records.
- **Lack of Realistic Goals or a Life Plan**
- **Criminal or Entrepreneurial Vulnerability** — changing their image to avoid prosecution.

Nearly every scammer I had been in contact with seemed to fall into any number of these categories, if not all of them. Dr. Mark R. Smith was a classic example of a sociopath, not to mention the other umpteen people I had any communication with during this time.

It was easy to see how these con artists could not get the kind of attention they craved, so they turned to abusing those people they envied. They are empty and damaged inside and beyond repair.

Hare and Gleckley went on to say:

"even though the sociopath can't be treated effectively with therapy, it doesn't mean that the rest of us can't protect ourselves from them. The most important factor in keeping a psychopath or sociopath at bay is to know your own vulnerabilities. Know our strengths so that our insecurities don't overcome us. Sociopaths are chameleons and become an image of what we haven't done for ourselves. Their appearance of perfection will begin to crack but by that time you will have been emotionally and perhaps financially scathed. There comes a time where there's no point in searching for answers. The only thing is to move on."

That might prove to be easier said than done.

# Moving On

*W*eeks had passed since my last word from Mark Smith. I was fascinated with his mental state, as I had recently learned of sociopathic behavior and had now totally detached myself from him emotionally. Yet I had been patiently waiting for his endgame and was still curious how it would be presented. Then I received what he had evidently been working on that would answer my question.

*My darling Gay,*

*You have showed me such love with your actions and yes it was always about love. I do love you sweetheart. I owe you so much more than money, I owe you my heart and my life and I understand if you are still angry with me, I deserve that but I can't live without you and I need to be with you to prove my love to you. You are such a special woman and I can't imagine my life without you in it. My failure was on my own side due to the journey I was on and having the experiences I can't explain but I can't afford to lose you my sweetheart. I made you a promise that I'm going to keep no matter the difficulties. I want to spend the rest of my life with you . . . I love you with all my heart and will never rest until I show you how much. We have this amazing bond that was there from the early stages of our relationship and I can't go on without you. Forgive me*

*again for not creating a time to see you before my
departure to England. I thought about it and realized I
made a mistake never to make in my whole life again
when I'm with you sweetheart. Try and see what you
can do for me, Babe, cause I am sick and tired of this
country and it is time for me to leave for good. I have
gone through a lot and I need out. Help me this once,
my queen, and the next call would be my arrival back
in the States and you can do to me whatever you wish
. . . I'm shedding tears now. I need your help, Babe.
Write me back when you can. I miss you so much and
I'll always love you.*

    *Yours forever.*
    *Mark*

Mark Smith had referenced the letter I had sent
which clearly stated that I was aware that he was a
scammer. Yet, he had tried to soften that up with
flowery words before trying, one last time, to solicit
money to help with his exit from Malaysia.

I am not sure how many times I read that email,
but enough times to confirm my belief that the behavior
of Mark R. Smith was that of a sociopath. It was
strange to think back over the past months. I had
wanted to find the right relationship, wanted to find
someone who I thought would be right for me. Enter
Dr. Mark R. Smith. I learned that he was nothing but
a total scam. Mark Smith was not a figment of my
imagination, but he never existed. I deleted the email
and put away the ghost of Mark R. Smith. I didn't need
or want them any more.

Not the ending I would have predicted. Perhaps he had just given up and realized there was nothing more to get from the current game. Maybe, and most likely, he had already gone on to create a new identity in pursuit of another love interest. Perhaps he had converted himself back into his former role as a contractor. It did not matter. What mattered to me is that I was safely out of it, and I knew I would be fine. I would turn my thoughts again toward writing about this experience, hoping that it might provide help and information to others who would follow the same road of internet dating. In any case it would be cathartic for me, and I thought a major step toward healing.

I felt comfortable without the drama of constant emails, chats and phone calls from the online 'characters'. I was relieved that I no longer had to endure lengthy "chats" while answers were being looked up. Strangely enough I felt most comfortable with the notion that I was exactly where I had started out some months ago. Alone.

My life was still full. I still had my friends and family around me, and of course there was always the constant and faithful Oliver. All was still right with my world.

# No Place Like Home

$O$scar and I still had never met. We also had never spoken on the phone — a point which I found increasingly disturbing. There was a time when he had spoken of taking me to Spain sometime.

"I want you to see my native country, my dear, I think you will love it."

*I know I will love it, I've been there, done that, but will not tell you that, you turkey, not now.*

"I have a trip coming up in a few weeks, I'll be working out of Madrid mostly, that's the big project I told you about, but we can travel throughout the country when I'm finished."

*If you can't pick up the phone to call me, how the hell do you think I'm dashing off to Spain to meet you in person?*

"Enjoy your trip, I hope it's successful, and call me when you get back — on the phone for a change." I thought that was specific enough for him. The part of being out of the country on extended business had a certain familiar ring to it, which had proven to be a negative situation in the past. My feelings toward him had decreased with every day that I did not see an opportunity presenting itself for either a meeting or a phone call. This 'business trip' was all the confirmation that I needed. One more major disappointment.

"Would you like to come to Spain *with* me?"

*That's out of left field but the answer is the same. Why would I do that — and what the hell would happen to me, or my safety, if I agreed to the trip?*

"Sure I would," I tossed it out to see what kind of response I would get and how fast he would back pedal.

"Well, do you want me to buy you the ticket, or reimburse you if you prefer to make your own travel arrangements?"

*You think you're a clever bastard but I'm wise to you, asshole.*

"I think you should go ahead and buy the ticket, that way we can travel together. I can always find things to do in Madrid while you're working, and we can have the evenings to ourselves." *See how that appeals to you.*

"We can talk about that later. I have to go to work now. Later, Bye."

*I bet it will be a cold day in hell before this discussion comes up again.*

I took a week off and went back to my hometown of Pittsburgh. I had not been back for a few years and the city was calling to me. I had friends and family I wanted to reunite with and now seemed the perfect time to do just that.

I loved how the downtown area had improved over the years. The tall glass and steel structures blended with the older more ornate stone buildings. The sun striking the renaissance-cleaned stone made every building sparkle as it rose tall against a late summer sky. The two new stadiums, PNC park and Heinz Field, were gorgeous facilities giving testimony to the city's love and dedication to sports. The Pirates and Steelers both had games in town the weekend I arrived, and I couldn't believe my luck in finding tickets for both events! I missed seeing the old hockey 'igloo' on this trip, but childhood memories of trying to skate on the Penguins' used ice, left a lasting impression on my mind and body, particularly on my buttocks, hips, and knees. Enough of an impression that I was satisfied to remain a baseball and football spectator. Pittsburgh was a serious sports loving town and, tragically, I was somewhat less of a serious ice skater.

I poured over old family photos of distinguished ancestors who had helped build and reshape the city during its renaissance, and spent countless hours amusing myself with family members and friends who shared my past. I had to believe it was better than strolling the streets of Madrid. I had wondered how my ancestors would have reacted to my recent months spent online with this foolishness. I doubt that their reaction would have been favorable.

The short week flew by, and the day I walked to the departure gate I nodded a final farewell to the same statue of Franco Harris who had smiled at me upon my arrival. I thought of the old but true cliché 'there really is no place like home'.

The minute I got back to Florida I went to the computer and sent off the following email that had written itself in my mind somewhere over the rolling hills of Pennsylvania:

*Mark:*

*I know that I will not hear from you ever again. You must recognize by now that I have known about you for some time. Months, really. Yet there were things that I wanted to tell you, and never did.*

*Love is a strange emotion. Powerful and forgiving, and not necessarily wise. Everything I ever told you was the truth, and from the heart. I know that is not something you are able to say. For you it was only a game; I was a means to your end. I believe that I was emotionally raped by you. That has been hard to deal with but I am dealing with it nonetheless.*

*I will close by telling you only this: I wish you well and encourage you to try to find a better path to follow in this life, and finally, I forgive you for what you did to me.*

*Gay*

I had no idea whatsoever why I did that, why I wrote it, or why I sent it, but it seemed ever so right at the time. I particularly don't know why I said: "I wish you well", when what I meant to say was I hoped he would get the jail sentence he deserved!

No one had ever done anything to me as horrible as this and I believe it was my way of working through it and offering forgiveness. I do know that a great sense of relief came over me when I hit 'send.' It was over. Finally.

*Now,* I could move on.

Part Three

# Solo

$\mathcal{I}$ was thinking of all the places in the world I still wanted to see, and I felt that if I had survived all of this. I could do anything. I could go anywhere. One thing I had not ever done was to travel any distance alone, always preferring the company of others. I had something to prove to myself now and I was ready to face that challenge. So, I booked a trip to Barcelona. I think some vision of online that Oscar might have prompted me to prove that I was perfectly capable of making my own arrangements and did not need him, or anyone, to accompany me. I had told Oscar not to contact me again. It had come on the heels of my friend Cathy finding the same photo of him, a duplicate of one I had previously sent her, only this photo appeared on a friend of Cathy's Facebook page in Canada! Whoever he was, he had clearly used someone's identity and created his profile to show him living in an affluent community outside Atlanta Georgia. Small world, thanks to the internet. I had lost all interest in tracking anything about him any further. I was over him, and all the others. It didn't matter. Enough was enough.

I booked my flight, decided to spend about five days in

Barcelona, a city I had heard wonderful things about but had never seen. There was a cruise that left Barcelona and headed east to the Italian Mediterranean coast which I had not seen: Tunisia and Morocco and the Canary Islands then back to Barcelona. It was two cruises back to back. The fare was very reasonable, it was October and I was a single woman, reborn and empowered. I packed the basics, said farewell to Oliver who would be staying with my daughter's family again, and off I went on my grand adventure. In spite of the last minute trepidations I experienced at the Miami airport I was moving forward, and somehow I knew I would be fine.

The city was more than I could have expected or anticipated. It was an architectural treasure with clean, wide streets and friendly and helpful people. It was a vibrant and thrilling place. I even got involved in a political demonstration over Spain's failed economy and high rate of unemployment. I had been out walking and learning about my new camera. The demonstration was a good opportunity to capture the excitement. Should my children ever wonder how their mother ended up on the CNN evening news in Barcelona, this might help explain it! I loved this city and somehow five days did not seem to be enough time.

The cruise was a continued opportunity to prove I had the ability and facility to meet strangers and I enjoyed myself immensely. I was on my own time schedule and loved that freedom. I was making this work.

At the conclusion of the trip I knew that I needed no one. I was a whole human being. I needed no one to validate me or make me feel important. I was fine. I was whole. I was capable. I no longer felt that I *needed* anyone in my life. I knew that I *wanted* someone. That was a major difference and a huge discovery. I wanted to share my life with someone special. I wanted to be able to shower affection on someone I really cared about. If it happened that would be fine, but there would be no more online dating sites to explore for a relationship. Not for me. I had been through that and, while it was an interesting experience, it is not anything I felt I wanted to repeat, ever again. No, my plan was to continue as I was. I would spend time with Oliver and our therapy work, and I would write about my online experiences. I had my family and my friends, I was a happy and whole person and I would be fine. Just fine.

The holidays came and went. I was busy and involved in my book. The unexpected phone call from Delsey gave me something new to think about.

"We're all going down to St. Croix for a week for this wedding," she said, "and we have rented a place near Cane Bay. Our whole family will be going. Why don't you think about coming along for the wedding? At least you'll know all of us, and you might have fun. It could be good for you to get away for a while."

I was startled at the offer and a bit hesitant, "I don't know right now. I just started back working on this book and I'm enjoying it, so don't know if I want to put it down for a week and go back to St. Croix. Been there, done that, and for thirty-seven years no less!"

"I know, I know, I said I would never go back either but here we are."

"Delsey, I was there about seven years ago and it was fine. I never said I wouldn't go back, but I feel like I did go back fairly recently."

"Well, at least think about it please, we'd love to have you join us and I think it would do you a world of good. Maybe you could use a change of pace."

Delsey was persuasive and really did not handle no very well. I did give it thought, and decided that perhaps I would go after all. I could use a break and there seemed to be a special on airfares. How convenient.

"I just booked my flight," I told her, "so I'll call you when I get there. I'm going to book into the little inn on the hill. That way I'm close to everything."

"I'm delighted you're going to be coming," Delsey sounded pleased, "and since you're coming we'll see that you get an invitation to the wedding. It's to be on the beach at sunset and it will be lovely."

"Thank you for that, but you need not include me in the ceremony I'd be perfectly content just hanging out with you all for a while and seeing some of my old friends."

"Gay, you're coming to the wedding. You'll have a good time and I'm very happy you decided to come along."

"Me too. I'm really looking forward to going back."

"I'm glad too. Besides, maybe you'll get a chance to see Vicente while you're down there."

There it was again, the tug at even the mention of his name. It seemed that recently he was always on my mind. It would be lovely to see him again. More than lovely. That was certainly an added incentive, though an improbable outcome.

It was in the back of my mind while I was giving the whole trip to St. Croix some thought. Some months after I had relocated to Florida, I had returned briefly to the island to visit friends and to fulfill a promise to a Rotarian who was assuming the presidency of my old club. I had made a call to Vicente, who had wasted no time in moving on with another woman in his life, and I was a bit surprised that he seemed eager then to meet me for lunch. We had a lovely visit over a sandwich and a few drinks and there still was an unmistakable spark between us, but he was not available, and I was still trying to get over him. The memory of that lunch and the unfulfilled possibilities, however, had lingered with me through the following years.

"It would be wonderful to see him again," I told Delsey. "I haven't heard from him in quite a while, and the phone number I have for him seems to have been disconnected. I'm not sure how to find him."

Still, finding him was foremost on my mind as I sat buckled in for take off.

# Reunion

$\mathcal{I}$ chose the window seat specifically so I might have the same experience flying into the island as if it was for the very first time. It looked the same at first glance. Hills and valleys were very green, goats were still wandering around abundantly, and the magnificent clouds were exactly as I had remembered. Huge puffs shaped into people profiles with big noses, kangaroos with large feet, a barking dog or a sleeping cat perhaps. You could see whatever you wanted to see in the clouds. We dipped over the western end of the island. The cruise pier had all been rebuilt after hurricane Hugo, and today there was even a ship in port. Many people were spilling into the quaint old town of Frederiksted with its gingerbread decorated shops, or walking to the neighboring beach for the day. It reminded me of the days that I had worked there with tourists, shuffling them around to catch their tours. Tourists were interesting people. They would approach me as I stood beside the American flag, to ask questions.

"Do you all speak English here?" and my other favorite, "Can we use American dollars here?"

I heard this so often I would have to look up to see if perhaps someone had indeed removed the flag and hoisted a different one in its place. They had not, of course. It was still an American Territory and these were just tourists on holiday, having left their brains back home. I'm sure the current batch of visitors was no different.

I waited for a very long time for my luggage, rented my car, pulled out into the left lane of traffic (some things never change) and was on my way.

I checked into my small inn with windows opening to a good view of the sea and accompanying breeze. I scanned the phone book for a current number for Vicente but the numbers that were listed did not work. I had made a few general inquiries along the way but no one had seen him for quite some time, no one knew for how long. I suspected he might have left the island. During one of our last phone conversations he had mentioned,

"We are hoping to leave the island at some point. I'm taking the extra two years after retirement to help me pay off the condo I bought. Then we were definitely leaving to go somewhere. Do you have any ideas for me?" He had heard me mention many times that Florida would be a good choice for him so I'm sure he would have let me know if that was his final decision. My guess is "they" had done just that, pulled up stakes and gone. I wanted to know, so the next day I pulled in to my friend's little shop to borrow her phone. I called Vicente's sister to get his number but could only leave a message for him; she had said he would probably be at work. My phone didn't work off the local satellite system which made most communication difficult to impossible. The following morning, after a few failed attempts to get through to each other, we finally connected. It had been nearly a year since I had heard his voice and I was excited to know I would possibly get to see him.

"Well, well, well," he sounded happy to hear me, a bit surprised that I had found him, and eager to see me.

"You better not be planning on leaving here any time soon." He was hoping there was still enough time to get together.

"I have a few days left but honestly I couldn't leave here without seeing you. You changed your number and I lost track of you."

"Well, you found me now, gal, so let's make the most of it. Can I take you to lunch?"

"I would love that. You know I'm dying to see you. Name the place and time."

After that was established, I finished my coffee and went to the closet to choose a pair of slacks and shirt. Something casual, yet flattering and smart. Vicente was quite the dapper dresser and always very complimentary about my clothes, both approving and complimentary of the finished product. I didn't want to disappoint.

The lunch date was set for exactly the same place where we had lunched seven years ago. The Bombay Club was a cozy little restored brick wine cellar in the center of the town of Christiansted. I dressed and headed into town for a few items I wanted to pick up before our lunch. I must have looked at my watch a hundred times and finally, close to the exact hour, heard that familiar voice calling out to me from across the street with his usual greeting:

"Hey, gal, I'm over here."

The feeling that came over me at the mere sound of his voice evoked the same emotion that came over me the day I first laid eyes on him. I knew that we were neighbors yet I had never seen him, until the morning when he had hailed me from his truck as I was walking my dog. He was on his way to work and he stopped to make eye contact with me. I saw his bright brown eyes and a smile that covered the whole of his finely chiseled face. I was utterly spellbound. I had a hard time breathing and trying to appear cool and calm at the same time.

"You have a very beautiful looking dog."

It was an odd pick up line but by week's end it had ultimately worked. That feeling now was just as powerful as it had been then. I couldn't get to him fast enough.

My heart began to pound as my feet flew across the street and I jumped into his arms. We stood there hugging for not nearly long enough, and then a quick kiss. He held me out at arms length.

"Let me get a good look at you, gal, you look terrific. Years younger somehow, what happened . . ."

"Nothing happened to me except a little time."

"Well, you just look, you *really* look good to me."

He was beginning to sound like he was in shock. I wasn't sure that was a compliment.

"You look damn good to me too, Vicente, I've missed you. Really missed you, and you haven't changed a bit. You scarcely look a day older." I felt I would melt into the sidewalk. Any residual feelings from the past that might have been responsible for our breakup were gone. Swept clean like a new floor. It seemed like the good old days were here again. We hugged again and walked inside to our table. He didn't take his eyes from me for the longest time. He seemed to be drinking me into his memory.

He was smiling that huge familiar smile, and after he asked me a barrage of questions, and again told me how fantastic I looked, we ordered a round of drinks.

"Gal, I can't believe you're here. Tell me again, what wedding is going on?"

"It's Rob's daughter, she's living here now, and Delsey called me and suggested I come down for the wedding. It turned out to be a great idea, don't you think?"

"I'm just glad to see you, however and why ever you came. It's been far too long. How long has it been anyway?"

"It's been seven or eight years now."

I wondered why he hadn't remembered that when it seemed so important to me. I guessed men had different thought processes than women.

He had not changed or aged one bit. He still had those good fine features, that endearing smile, caramel colored skin and those gorgeous eyes. His head was still cleanly shaved. There was no doubt he was still a handsome man and he looked better than good to me. I wondered if he would always have this kind of affect on me.

We had nearly a decade of information to share between us. I told him about my recent experience with online dating, that it had not worked for me at all, and that I was still alone. He had been alone for a year, by choice, and working on staying to himself, avoiding trouble and just trying to be a better man including changing old behavior. So there it was. He had broken it off with his old girlfriend. There was currently no woman in his life! The Pina Colada slid down very easily as I reviewed the key phrase in my mind: 'no woman in his life.' So *now* he was available. I had waited eight long years to hear that, and now that I had heard it, I couldn't say or do anything, just smile. Thank God I had made this trip!

Lunch was a tasty seafood salad for us both, followed by another round of drinks and a suggestion that I might like to see his condo. That could have been a loaded invitation, or just a simple invitation. Either way, I eagerly obliged and off we went.

The condo was very close to town, on the second floor, with a dramatic view of Christiansted.

"You have a marvelous view of the town, Vicente, this is just fabulous. You must love it here."

"I love sitting here and watching the traffic, the boats, and listening to the sounds in town most days. It's very restful."

The sailboats moored in the harbor were pushed slowly back and forth by the same perfect breeze that swept through the patio as we sipped our drinks and continued sharing stories of our last seven or eight years.

"Tell me how you got into that online stuff, Gay. That seems like a bad idea."

"It was a bad idea," and then I quickly added, "it

was a bad idea that became a good thing. It was something I had to go through and I learned a lot. So it's a good thing that came from a bad idea."

"How did you ever think it would be a good idea?" Vicente was interested in this process mainly because it was not a feasible situation for an island, with such a small data base.

"I did it for only one reason."

"Which is . . .?"

"I was trying to get over you.  Believe it or not I have not found one person in the whole state of Florida that I thought was interesting. No one has caught my eye, so I did the only thing I could think of to try to move on."

"It's hard for me to believe that no one has crossed your path."

"Well, believe it, because it's true."

"I guess they're all crazy there."

"I'll take that as a compliment," and smiled.

We laughed at many things, how Delsey had pushed me into this online business by way of her television program, how Sam had participated in it as well, and all the ups and downs I met with along the way. We agreed that it was best for any problems that we'd had in the past to remain in the past. There would be time enough for those conversations later. It was just too wonderful to be spending time together for now, and we savored every minute.

I was standing next to him looking out at the night crawling in and I took his hand and turned to him.

"When we broke up . . ."

"Shhh," he interrupted, putting his finger to his lips, "I don't want to talk about that now."

He took my face in his hands and kissed me, softly at first, then with more passion. I looked at him and forced myself to continue.

"No, I have to tell you this, V., and I may not get another chance. When we broke up, it seemed so wrong. It felt all wrong. Everything was wrong. It has seemed wrong ever since, and I have just been floundering, and . . . " but I could not finish my sentence. I was a mess. Tears were running down my face and all my words were jumbled into one gasp after another.

"I know," he said, "but here we are now. It's okay." He stopped talking and just held me. We stood there together in the night, pressed between the memory of our past and the uncertainty of our future.

"Would you like to see the rest of the place?" It was a mood changer but perhaps a good thing.

"Sure I would. Lead the way."

I knew that his Dutch background would not allow him to live in anything less than neat and tidy. I had lived with him for years and knew he was particular in that way. It was a fine quality.

The tour of the spotlessly clean and nicely furnished condo, along with my cursory inspection of his bedroom and bathroom, supported his statement that there was no woman currently in his life. We did exchange a glance that put me on alert this would undoubtedly *not* be the last time I was in this bedroom. I would leave that alone for now.

"There's a jump up in town tonight, do you want

to go?" He asked rather hopefully.

A jump up is a local island street party where shops stay open, people sell food and drink items on the streets, and different musical groups perform throughout the town. It was always well attended and I thought it would be great fun to return to town later and participate, maybe grab a bite to eat and probably catch a few of my friends. It was one of those events that everyone loved to attend because they knew they would see everyone there!

"I'd love to go" I said. "I always loved the jumpups and no doubt I'll run into a few of my friends. You wouldn't mind that would you?"

Vicente was sometimes cautious about being seen places, he had held a high profile job in the past and could never go anywhere without being recognized. I wasn't sure about this separation from his former girlfriend and how that might affect things for him, or perhaps he was seeing someone new.

"I'd love to take you to jump up. The music is always great, we could both stand a bit of dinner, so let's go."

We headed back into town and walked along the boardwalk hand in hand. It seemed so natural. It appeared like every resident and every tourist had the same idea about this night. The streets were packed. Music came from every corner. Brightly costumed Mocko Jumbies (African stilt dancers) were performing on one end of the street and we stood a moment to watch. I caught up with a few of my friends passing by, who smiled at the two of us being together again, then they moved on, drinks in hand, to form their own conclusions about what was *really* going on between us. A fine example of island melée. We were there for hours, wandering, drinking, visiting, dancing and having fun. When finally it was time to leave this street party, there was no doubt that it would be to make our own music and have out own party, in private.

It had been eight long years since I had felt a man moving inside me. Though he refused to believe it, this man Vicente had been the last. While he was not the first man I had ever been with, he made it impossible now to even remember any other. Every inch of his hard, well-toned body was comforting and familiar and I welcomed him to me like rain to a parched land. Vicente had always been the best lover I'd ever had.

He was passionate, and tender. Lovemaking was delicious and delirious; he was exactly what I wanted and needed. I felt the tension and stress of the past months slip away; replaced by a state of sheer and utter euphoria and contentment that can only be achieved through the skill of a very satisfying lover.

I was insatiable. He was obliging. I had dreamed about this moment with him for eight years, even though I was sure it likely would never come. Yet, here we were. I could not remember being happier.

The night became morning and when dawn broke it was time for me to leave. I was sad that the night had ended and thrilled to have been with him after all these years, yet uncertain of what lay ahead.

I returned to the inn to begin my packing. I had a flight

to catch. I packed each item as a careful memory being stored for eternity.

Later, when I would reach for one of these pieces of clothing I hoped it would remind me of this very special time shared with Vicente. He had sent me a text message which asked me to call him. I hurried to finish the packing then got to the phone.

"I really enjoyed being with you," he began, "and I don't want you to go. Do you have to go?"

"Well, I don't *have* to go," I was not looking forward to leaving him either but changing a ticket would be a hassle and an expense.

"I'll see what I can do about changing my ticket, if you're sure."

I hoped his question came from the heart, rather than a copulatory response from his year of celibacy.

"I'm not sure where any of this is headed," he said, "but we sure could use some more time to talk about things, don't you agree?"

"Yes, I do agree; let me get to work on the ticket change."

I had hoped that this wouldn't be the end of a beautiful few days. It seemed like there was so much still alive between us, as if nothing had changed, and yet many things had changed. We had become wiser to the ways of the world, and wiser about each other. My recent online experience had opened my eyes to treachery and deceit but had confirmed my desire to have a man in my life again. I had spent some years on my own since leaving the island and believe I had grown as a result.

How could I refuse him? We had had a wonderful time together and we still had many things to talk over and possibly resolve. My feelings for him had not changed. I hoped his had not either. There was only one way to find out. I was at his condo within twenty minutes, suitcase in hand.

His greeting was passionate, welcoming and exciting. Clearly he was glad I was able to rearrange my flight and that I wanted to stay longer. Hauling my suitcase up several flights of stairs seemed effortless to him. He was in great shape and very strong. He had maintained his youthful exuberance, which is one of the many things I loved about him. At the top of the last flight of stairs, he put down the suitcase, stuck the key in the door, turned to me, and asked an odd question.

"So it seems to me that you were having some sort of religious experience last night. Did you? Is that what it was?"

"Religious experience?" I was a bit surprised, "No, that was the furthest thing from my mind. Why do you ask?"

I saw his lips curve upward in an expansive crescent-sized smile as his answer came.

"Because all night, all I heard you say was, Oh God, Oh God!"

His humor was not wasted on me.

I couldn't help thinking about that last night, or the three rapturous days that followed. Whatever else would happen, we at least had this time.

It sure turned out to have been one hell of a lunch!

# Old Fire-Stick

$\mathcal{M}$y last days with Vicente were wonderful and languorous. We laughed about all old silly things between us, visited some mutual friends, enjoyed the beaches, island food and drink, and most especially we enjoyed being together and making love. We spoke of what it might be like to move forward together and how we would try to make it work in the short run with so many miles of ocean separating us. For me, I was sure of my feelings for him; those feelings had not changed. There was still that magical spark that, for me, is a key ingredient to any relationship. The spark that had been missing all these years. Before this trip to the island I had spent eight years working hard to get over him. Finally, after not meeting *anyone* who held my interest, I had involved myself with the online exercise, with a peculiar outcome — far from any I might have anticipated. It was not all bad because arguably that experience was a turning point in my life. I knew now what I wanted and what I did not want. I also learned throughout the process that I was ready, and desirous of being in a real relationship with a man. Suppressed feelings within me had been awakened and I found that I missed not having a man in my life. I wanted to be in love again and to give and receive love. That was a wonderful feeling.

All things happen for a reason. The online experience forced me to get to know myself. I had to spend time really searching myself in ways most people don't always have the opportunity of doing. I was grateful to the relatively slow pace in which I was drawn through my early childhood. I was given time to savor so many things. The initial pitfall, if I should label it that way, was going too quickly from my parental home to my married home. I grew into my role of motherhood with every diaper change and scraped knee, but that process took my total attention and focus; there was little leftover for myself. In hindsight, I could have used a bit more time *before* my children to really sort out who I was. Who I became was a mother. I loved that role, and I loved my children beyond any sensible measure. Looking back on those years I would not have changed one moment of it. I cherished each moment with them. If I had been more aware of who I was as a person, I wonder if I could have then been able to share that with my children, and thus become a *better* mother. The children thrived and succeeded in spite of my inexperience.

From that point on I was on a path of raising children, assimilating into a new community, taking on a new business, surviving natural disasters, divorce, a career change, and an ultimate relocation away from the only adult life I really knew. It took great courage to leave the Caribbean, a place that I not only loved but that had become a part of me. It was only after I had stopped shuffling furniture around and meeting new friends in Florida that I found time to sit and 'smell the coffee.' It was only after I had a moment to focus on me that I became involved with the online adventure. Quirky, and as potentially dangerous and undesirable as much of that was for me, again, I would not have changed one moment. That has brought me to this place and this place seems right, and that feels good to me.

There is an expression in the West Indies: "Old Fire-stick, easy to catch" which quite literally means that if you have been in a relationship with someone previously, it will be easier to catch them again, the second time around. Just the same as an old fire-stick will catch fire more quickly than a young green twig. The simplicity of these West Indian expressions is fabulous. What an interesting and colorful approach to life.

It is certainly true that Vicente and I had seamlessly re-ignited our relationship. He had used the phrase *Que sera, sera.* What will be will be. He seemed unsure of what the future would hold but knew everything in the universe was about timing. What I needed to know was if our time together had been one of longing, and maybe just a lusty lunch, or had it been something more. I knew that for me, nothing had changed. I still loved him. There was only one way for me to really know how *he* felt, and that would require my return to the island, this time for two weeks.

"If he is not right for me, do not put him in my path." I kept saying that over and over, and I held on to that.

"I have a flat, a flat, so hang on, I'm on my way," Vicente had been screaming into my mobile voicemail.

I believed he would be along shortly so I picked up some island information on tours just for fun.

While glancing through the pages, my mind raced backward, about twenty years, to my ex-spouse who never wanted to pick me up at the airport. Ever. I had to hope today would have a better outcome.

"There you are, Sweetie, I'm filthy dirty and apologize for the blasted flat but give me a hug anyway please." His smile was as broad and as endearing as ever.

"Oh God, it's good to see you again gal. Who cares about a little dirt, and give me a kiss while you're at it, I've waited weeks for this."

My arms wrapped around him and I thought it was one of the nicest airport pickups I could ever remember, even if a bit dirty and a bit late.

"You look great in those jeans, lady," he mentioned in an admiring manner.

"Well, thank you kindly Sir, I guess I probably wear them a bit better than the last time you saw me." His manners prevented him from commenting on the comparison, but we both knew I had shed some pounds since the last time we had been together and some serious pounds in the last eight years.

"I have dinner all prepared, so I hope you've worked up an appetite during the flight." A guy who can cook! This would be easy to get used to.

"I'm impressed that you're still cooking. You were always very good in the kitchen . . . and the bedroom, I should add!"

"Anything for you, Sweetie, I'm just happy you are here."

"I'm happy too, I really wanted to come back to see you, we do have many things to sort through, but first, let's get to your dinner!"

The weather was lovely, still a bit cool, and the humidity still low. Clear skies, and as the local weather reporter said daily, ". . . with a twenty percent chance of rain." That was the standard cover-your-ass report we used to have televised daily. The weather was always about the same, save a hurricane or other major disturbance.

Vicente was right, he had certainly prepared dinner. It was pleasant enough to sit outside again and share ideally seasoned meat and vegetables, also known locally as "provisions." These were potatoes, onions, carrots, beans, corn, all braised in the pot and very savory. A side dish of fried plantain topped off the meal along with a bottle of wine.

"I hope you like pot roast," he asked. "I worked on it early this morning."

"I love pot roast and this is particularly good. You're really good. I will have another glass of wine, please, then I want to show you what I brought you."

He poured two glasses of red wine and made some room at the table for some reading material I had brought with me.

"I brought a number of brochures and books for you to go through, at your leisure, so you could get an idea of what kind of opportunities would be available to you in Florida."

He took a few in his hands and said, "You seem to have thought of everything. Am I going to Florida now?"

"I thought we had mentioned that just a bit, the last time, and I know you once were eager to leave here. You mentioned it again last time I was here, so I thought I would at least let you know what was in Florida that might interest you."

I was quite pleased with myself for having put this into motion and for collecting all the materials and hauling them to St. Croix.

I was not sure how this was being received.

"I think it is a good idea, thanks for bringing it but it won't be that easy for me to just jump up and disappear like that." My heart began to sink.

"What do you mean by that? I thought you could go whenever you wanted?"

"Theoretically, but this is a horrid time to sell real estate, even to rent. I have another job, which you know, and I can't just run out on all this. I have bills to pay and responsibilities here."

"I guess I thought you were closer to wanting to leave than you are now telling me." I was a bit distressed over his response because it seemed a bit open ended.

"Well, no harm in just looking through the material when you feel like it." I was still hopeful. "You never know what might strike your fancy."

We spoke about a few things we wanted to do for fun during our time together, and agreed that one ground rule that we should follow again would be to let the past remain there. We had our hands full working on the future without dredging up old questions like "why did you do this" back then. We also agreed that the most important item on the agenda that would not wait any longer was our physical needs. It had been one full month since we had last been together, but somehow the rush to undress made it seem like it had been far longer.

Two weeks flew quickly. We did the same things we had done when I had been there the first time. Beach, shopping, touring, visiting, talking, and nothing at all. I enjoyed it because we were together and the conversation confirmed that many behaviors of his past that had been problematic had indeed been corrected. I was encouraged, pleased for him, and hopeful. We talked about many things, mostly his current job, and *if* by chance we could make this work again, what would be the necessary steps to get him off the island, and what would be the timeframe.

"Did we ever talk this much before?" he asked, then added "I really don't remember that we sat and just had long conversations like we are having now."

"I'm quite sure we didn't discuss the same sort of things, and certainly didn't go into anything in depth. Do you think that might have been part of our problem? We just didn't take the time to talk things through in the right way." I wondered about that, and added, "Maybe we were too involved with our day to day lives, work, parties and things, and didn't spend enough time making plans, or talking about the future."

When I finished my thoughts it sounded right and sensible. Vicente did not disagree.

"I'm guessing that's true," he said, "but what a shame we waited all this time to get things right."

"We were younger then" I added, "and maybe it didn't seem to matter so much, even though it should have." I couldn't think of any other rational explanation.

"We were younger, we were also different people, with different interests, and living in the moment. I don't believe you ever thought much about a long term future together, but that's what I always wanted. I think you were simply going along for the ride, enjoying life day by day for however long that would last. I didn't think I could change your mind and I certainly didn't want to force you into something you weren't ready to commit to so I just followed along with you, enjoying the time."

"I suppose you're right." Then, he added "I can only hope we do better this time. I know I want to. I'm ready to have a different life than the one I lived before. I'm a better man than that. That's why I spent nearly a year on my own. I was concentrating on what didn't work, and on what I wanted. I want to be a better man and I believe that I can be that man now."

That was the best thing I heard him say, and I certainly agreed. I also wanted to do much better. I wanted a permanent relationship. I knew I could be a better partner now. I felt we always had something special together, had from the beginning. Life got in the way, things changed, then when we were ready, life brought us together again.

"I believe there's a reason I agreed to come back to this island the first time, for that wedding." I said with conviction, "I don't believe in accidents."

I was positive my trip to St. Croix was a plan of the universe.

"We are where we are meant to be at a certain time, and *this* is where I was meant to be. I was meant to go online, and all of that stumbling around was the way the universe had of keeping me distanced enough from those unreal people, until finally I would be in the middle of *your* path, and we would meet again."

I was certain of that now; it all made perfect sense.

"What's the next step?" Vicente eyed me curiously.

I began with my first thought: "I think it's logical for you to come to Florida and stay a while." *I believed it was a bit more important, even critical perhaps, than just logical.*

"I don't know how much time you can take off but I think it's important."

A Florida lifestyle would be similar to the one he was familiar with, yet there were bound to be differences and adjustments.

"I don't see why coming to Florida is *that* important, I can be anywhere that you are." He sounded genuine, and it felt like a lovely thing to hear, but I was firm on this point.

"I believe you need to come to Florida to reassure yourself that it is a lifestyle that you would be comfortable with. That you feel good in the same environment where I am living."

The last thing I would want would be for him to come to Florida, change his mind, and leave to go back to the island. That would be horrible. For both of us.

I was getting the sense that perhaps he felt we had spent a bit too much time on this subject for now. Venus and Mars came to mind and the different way men and women process information. Vicente is less verbal than I but dwells longer on the subject. I probably beat it to death with my repetitive tongue, where he would study it over a long time, until he felt the time was right to act. I had learned a few things over these years, among them, when it was time to fold. That time had come. I knew I had probably overwhelmed him with my summary of the big picture. It was the last thing I wanted to do. Vicente needed time to process this, slowly. The subject was dropped.

In the remaining days we spoke of a future unfolding in Florida. He could easily find a job anywhere, and we could travel in his time off and have a wonderful life. We knew it would take some time to execute this plan but we agreed that it was what we wanted to do. We had a plan and were moving forward, however slowly.

"I have never seen you quite like this," I told him when we got to the airport.

"What's the matter? You look so serious and upset and didn't say much of anything the whole way here."

"I can't take this," he said, "I just don't want you to go, I don't want to say good-bye."

He had never been big on expressing deep emotion or feelings, preferring actions over mushy words, so I had never had an occasion to see this side of him. It was unnerving, a bit maddening, but somehow touching.

I wrapped my arms around him.

"You said you will come to Florida soon, quickly as you can, then it will be all right. We need to spend more time together and you could use a change of scene. I'll really miss you, and you know I love you."

"I love you too, Sweetie, and I'm sorry for acting all quiet and shitty this morning. I will miss you, you know I will."

With little more than a tearful kiss and a bear hug I was off through security, and didn't see him again.

During the flight home I began to wonder if I ever would.

It had been one year since my journey first began.

I had survived it all, along with Oliver. Now he sits patiently by the front door eager to begin his walk. His patience and my optimism are unwavering.

I know he is waiting for my hand to turn that handle. Smiling down at him I remind him of an earlier promise that I had made to him.

"Today will be a good day," I had said, "when we get back to the house you can curl up on the bed and watch me clean out my closet, again. I want to make some room for my old fire-stick. Just in case!"

He rotates his fox-like tail with great enthusiasm, and in doing so, has agreed with me one more time.

THE END

# *Final Note*

The internet is full of data accumulated by men and women who have been scammed by novices and experts alike. We owe it to ourselves to be vigilant as possible, and above all, to listen to our skeptical friends and family members who warn us, out of love and concern.

To everyone who will enter into this process to find the perfect match, I would encourage you to stop and listen to your own inner voice, no matter how weak or faint the sound.

This was my personal journey through online dating sites. It was enlightening, humorous, fascinating, dangerous, empowering, and totally survivable.

To those of you who would attempt a similar journey I would tell you to enjoy the experience, and may one of those slippery frogs turn into *your* handsome Prince.

R.G. Graham

# Acknowledgments

I would like to thank Patrika Vaughn for her technical suggestions and editing, without whose help this book would not have been printed.

I am grateful to my special group of friends who nourished me along the way with their interest, encouragement, advice and warning. Dulcy, Roland, Jerry, Geri, Cathy, and Polly, are joined by an ever widening circle of friends who shared their wisdom, concerns and opinions freely with me out of kindness and love. You are all imbedded in my heart.

Finally, I am indebted to my family for their advice, suggestions and support during this journey as well as the process of writing this book. I dedicate this book to Rachel, Charles, Nissa, Roger and, in particular, to the memory of my mother who encouraged me from childhood to always write about my adventures.

CPSIA information can be obtained at www.ICGtesting.com
Printed in the USA
LVOW13s0725181013

357422LV00001B/1/P